# Foreword

The Health & Safety Executive (HSE) is pleased to see industry preparing supporting guidance for designers. CIRIA has a reputation for preparing useful "good practice" guidance, and it is noted that the existing CDM guidance for designers is being updated both as guidance for designers as they consider hazards and risks arising during construction (this guide), and during the use of a structure as a workplace (a new companion guide).

It is hoped that designers will use this guidance to raise their awareness of the issues they have to address; designers need to be aware of the hazards and risks which affect those involved in all aspects of construction, including maintenance.

CDM2007 is designed to bring the consideration of the actual potential hazards and risks on each project to the forefront of a designer's work and this guide should assist designers in carrying out their duties by seeking to eliminate hazards, minimise the risks which remain and communicate residual risks to others. This activity must be at the core of a designer's work whether on a small house extension or an Olympic stadium.

**Health & Safety Executive**

**British Library Cataloguing in Publication Data**
A catalogue record is available for this book from the British Library.

# About this guide

## THE CDM REGULATIONS

The Construction (Design and Management) Regulations 2007 (known as CDM2007 in this guide) affect construction work in the UK. The Regulations place duties upon all designers and this guide is designed to assist in fulfilling those duties with respect to construction work.

CDM2007 builds upon earlier health and safety legislation by imposing a framework of duties so that all the parties to a construction project must consider health and safety. The Regulations have an Approved Code of Practice L144 (known as the ACoP) titled *Managing Health and Safety in Construction: Construction (Design and Management) Regulations 2007*, which has legal status and must be referred to alongside CDM2007.

Guidance has been prepared by industry working groups and may be freely accessed through <www.citb-constructionskills.co.uk/CDM>.

**This guide addresses construction hazards; there is a companion CIRIA guide C663 (*CDM2007 – Workplace "in-use" guidance for designers*) which addresses workplace "in-use" hazards, ie risks to those who work in or are affected by structures in use, as now required by CDM2007.**

## READERSHIP

Construction work sector guidance for designers is written for those wishing to develop a full understanding of the designer function with respect to relevant construction hazards under CDM. It focuses upon the management of hazard and risk but also provides information about designers' CDM duties in general. The term designer is a defined term under CDM2007 and has a broad meaning, going beyond the traditional meaning to include anyone who makes input to design decisions. This is discussed in the guidance. It should also be noted that during the stages of a project, different designers will be active; initially consultants may be making conceptual decisions and working up schemes, but later trade contractors will be designing their work and the main contractor will be designing site systems including lifting arrangements. It is the job of the CDM coordinator to coordinate these inputs.

Each designer will have his or her own area of decision-making, which will affect risks on site, both during construction and during subsequent activities, including cleaning and other maintenance work, alteration and demolition. Designers need to concentrate on the decisions that they can influence while being aware of the concerns of other designers, which may be affected by their actions.

A general understanding of CDM2007 and its ACoP L144 is assumed. For further information see the section "Sources of further information". In particular, when considering workplace "in-use" risks (ie those risks which remain after construction and affect those using the structure), designers may refer to the CIRIA publication C663: *CDM2007 – workplace "in-use" guidance for designers.*

## KEY POINTS

It must be understood that anyone who acts as a designer as defined by CDM2007 (including a client who imposes specific requirements) has duties as a designer under CDM.

*All those who contribute to design decisions affecting construction must consider the hazards and risks involved. This requires an understanding of construction work, including subsequent activities (maintenance including cleaning, alteration and demolition) and of the types of accidents and health issues that are involved.*

This report provides a wealth of accessible information about health and safety issues in a wide range of construction activity. The consideration of these matters must be an integral part of the design decision process. Each designer has a part to play, working as a member of the design team who must make decisions related to health and safety in a coordinated manner, led by the CDM coordinator.

The object of CDM is to *embed health and safety management into projects*. All designers have a role to play and must communicate with others to provide information about health and safety for contractors to take into account, as they plan and execute work on site.

A designer's duties under CDM require considerable common sense and openness in order to relate to the other duty-holders in a constructive manner. *Duties must be carried out in a manner that is proportional to the type of project and the likely level of risk.*

Information prepared by designers for the purposes of CDM must:

❑ focus on health and safety information that competent people would not reasonably anticipate
❑ be specific to the project
❑ reflect the level of risk and complexity
❑ be concise.

Particular care is needed to prepare **concise, focused documentation that is relevant to the project in hand**. In this way it will be of immediate use to the people who need to use it. To achieve this, the use of lengthy standardised or off-the-shelf catch-all documents **must be avoided.** The aim is to produce relevant information that is proportionate to the project and its risks, and hence useful and cost-effective.

## HOW TO USE THIS GUIDE

The guide has been structured so that it can be read from cover to cover or consulted by those who simply need to dip in for specific information. It is divided into sections that focus on construction work sectors and, for each project, only the relevant sectors need be consulted. The guidance is designed to provoke thought and to improve understanding and knowledge; it cannot provide complete information for every circumstance. As with all checklist guidance, the user must ask "is there anything else, for this particular project?"

### Chapter 1 – Introduction
This chapter introduces the duties of a designer under CDM and suggests how the guidance may be used in managing hazard and risk. It provides information about over-arching issues, the planning and sequencing of construction, common causes of accidents and the major health hazards in construction.

### Chapter 2 – Construction work sector guidance
A wide range of construction activities are examined, by sector. For each sector, major hazards are identified and discussed, risk mitigation measures are proposed and reference to further guidance is provided.

### Chapter 3 – Providing information
Advice is given about the need for decisions to be documented, including the statutory duty to provide health and safety information to others.

### Chapter 4 – Sources of further information

Appendices:  A Checklist of hazard management
             B Checklist of information to be provided
             C Examples of hazard elimination and risk
               reduction on projects.

# Acknowledgements

The original research work leading to this publication was carried out by Ove Arup and Partners, under contract to CIRIA. The project supervisor was Allan Delves assisted by Paul Craddock and publication design was by Steven Groak. CIRIA's research manager for the project was David Churcher.

The book was updated in 2003 to align with the amendments to the CDM Regulations in 2000 and the revised ACoP published in 2001. The contractor for this work was Alan Gilbertson of Gilbertson Consultants Limited and CIRIA's research manager was David Storey.

The book was updated again by Alan Gilbertson in 2007 to align with the rewritten CDM Regulations and their ACoP.

## 2007 Project Steering Group

This current 2007 update was guided by a Steering Group established by CIRIA to advise on technical issues. CIRIA and Gilbertson Consultants Limited would like to express their thanks and appreciation to all members of the Project Steering Group and their organisations.

This comprised:

| | |
|---|---|
| Paul Craddock | Arup |
| Matt Harrison | Arup |
| David Lambert | Kier Group |
| Andrew Stevens | Atkins |
| Bob Keenan | Sheppard Robson |
| Peter Sheaves | Consultant |
| David Watson | WSP |
| John Carpenter | Consultant. |

Andrew East and colleagues at the Health and Safety Executive also provided valuable assistance.

# Contents

**LIST OF FIGURES**

**LIST OF TABLES**

# 1    Introduction

## 1.1    THE PURPOSE, SCOPE AND LIMITATIONS OF THIS GUIDANCE

This guidance has been produced to assist designers to comply with Regulation 11 of the Construction (Design and Management) Regulations 2007, (CDM2007). This Regulation requires designers to ensure that any design prepared for the purposes of "construction work" during construction, maintenance, repair or demolition includes adequate regard to the avoidance of hazards and the reduction of risk during construction. This guidance touches on duties other than those under Regulation 11, to set the duties in context. The scope of a designer's responsibility under CDM2007 is examined fully in the Approved Code of Practice (ACoP) L144, which all practicing designers should be familiar with – see in particular paragraphs 110–145.

The duty to consider risks to users of completed structures is dealt with in a companion CIRIA publication C663 entitled *CDM2007 – Workplace "in-use" guidance for designers.*

The purpose of this guidance is to help designers to manage health and safety risks during construction work, arising from their designs, while meeting their statutory duty, in the following ways.

1   It provides information on the major hazards associated with each of the specific construction work areas.

2   It gives key considerations, prompts and examples to encourage designers to think about the peculiarities of their own specific projects and to identify and prioritise project-related hazards, with respect to the stages of design.

3   Once the health and safety hazards have been identified, it provides signposts to the types of responses that designers can make to alter their design to avoid, reduce or control the hazards.

4   It gives cross-references to other sectors of construction work addressed by the report, which may be related in terms of health and safety, and to external texts from which more detailed information may be obtained.

The guidance has been drafted for designers who are active in design practice in any construction discipline and need rapid access to the key considerations connected with a particular construction work sector. Within each sector, what the designer can achieve is influenced by the design stage and previous decisions that have been made, either by the designer or by others.

The scope of this report is restricted to 39 construction work sectors, chosen following industry consultation and intended to represent those areas of construction work considered to contain the most significant and common hazards and risks to the health and safety of construction workers and others (eg members of the public and building occupiers). However, these construction work sectors by no means address all hazards in construction. Every designer has to think through the design options to identify all the hazards that can reasonably be foreseen and then act accordingly to avoid or reduce them.

A number of the hazards mentioned specifically in the work sectors, or those that designers may further identify, may be outside a particular designer's scope of control or may be issues that a contractor would deal with. However, they are included so that designers may be as fully informed as possible about the range of potential hazards. Those not familiar with site practices might find *Health and Safety in construction*, HSG150, a useful introduction to the main health and safety hazards in construction work.

The designer's duties relate to considering construction hazards that can reasonably be identified and to providing information so that contractors and others can be made aware of them. Designers are not required to outline methods of dealing with hazards but should explain any particular construction assumptions that have been made as part of the design.

Readers need to appreciate that the guidance in this document is not intended to repeat information available elsewhere, but to include reference to it, so it is not intended that this handbook can be read entirely in isolation.

## 1.2 DEFINITIONS

### 1.2.1 Designer

CDM2007 defines the term "designer" with much wider meaning than that common in construction usage. See Section 1.4.2 for an explanation of the term designer.

### 1.2.2 Construction work

CDM2007 likewise defines (Reg 2) the term "construction work" with much wider meaning than that common in construction usage, including maintenance, cleaning and decoration. Designers are expected to consider hazards to those who maintain, repair, clean, refurbish, adapt and eventually remove or demolish all or part of a structure, as well as those who construct it.

### 1.2.3 Stages of a project

The terms "concept stage", "scheme stage" and "detail stage" have been used in this guide to subdivide the design process. It should be noted that much design (in its widest sense) is done after the appointment of contractors. The designer's response to any hazards identified will vary according to the stage of design development. There is more flexibility to avoid hazards at the start of the design process during concept stage, than during the detail stage when control measures may be more appropriate for dealing with any remaining hazards.

## 1.3 THE CONTINUING NEED FOR ACTION TO IMPROVE HEALTH AND SAFETY IN CONSTRUCTION

The chances of being killed during a working lifetime on construction sites are currently around 1 in 650 and the chances of being disabled by serious illness or injury is much greater than for workers in other industries. In addition, members of the general public are also injured and killed by construction work. Figures from the Health and Safety Executive indicate that on average (2003/4 to 2005/6) 66 workers are killed on sites each year.

An analysis of this figure by types of accident is given in Table 1.1. Although the total number and mix of fatalities varies each year, the nature of accidents has remained broadly the same.

**Table 1.1**   *Analysis of figures by type of accident*

| Percentage of total | Type of accident |
|---|---|
| 46% | Falls from a height |
| 15% | Struck by falling/flying object, eg during machine lifting of materials |
| 6% | Contact with electricity or an electrical discharge |
| 15% | Struck by a moving vehicle |
| 9% | Trapped by something collapsing or overturning |
| 2% | Contact with moving machinery or material being machined |
| 7% | Other causes |

There is also a large incidence of health problems amongst construction workers and Table 1.2 gives estimates for numbers suffering ill-health as a result of certain hazards. These numbers dwarf the figures for injuries and on-the-job fatalities and in many cases, the effects may not be felt until years of exposure has taken place.

**Table 1.2**   *Estimates of numbers of construction workers suffering ill-health*

| Hazard (possible resulting disease or condition) | Annual estimates | |
|---|---|---|
| | Lower limit | Upper limit |
| Asbestos (mesothelioma, asbestosis, lung cancer) | 200 (deaths) | 250 (deaths) |
| Musculoskeletal injury (back disorders, work-related upper limb disorders, lower limb disorders) | 55 000 | 70 000 |
| Respiratory disease (bronchitis, emphysema, asthma, pneumoconiosis, sinusitis, influenza) | 3500 | 23 000 |
| Skin disease | 3100 | 10 500 |
| Noise (deafness and ear conditions) | 1000 | 5800 |
| Vibration conditions | 200 | 400 |

From the figures in these tables, it is clear that great improvements can be made. To do so, contributions need to be made by clients, designers and contractors. In particular designers need access to guidance that will help them identify the hazards arising from their design and then to avoid, reduce or control these hazards through the design process.

## 1.4   THE DESIGNER'S DUTIES UNDER CDM2007

### 1.4.1   The importance of design in managing health and safety in construction.

CDM2007 places the designer at the centre of health and safety, jointly with the contractor, because the work to be done is of the designer's choosing. The ACoP states:

"Designers are in a unique position to reduce the risks that arise during construction work, and have a key role to play in CDM… Designers' earliest decisions can fundamentally affect health and safety… [Designers] need to consider the health and safety of those who will maintain, repair, clean, refurbish and eventually demolish all or part of a structure... Designers have to weigh many factors as they prepare their designs. Health and safety considerations have to be weighed alongside other considerations, including cost, fitness for purpose, aesthetics, buildability, maintainability and environmental impact...". (ex paragraphs 109–111 and 124).

***All designers need to be familiar with CDM2007 and the ACoP, or they will not be able to undertake the legally enforceable duties placed upon them by CDM.***

## 1.4.2  Who are designers?

It is important to appreciate who is classed as a designer. As well as the design team appointed by a client (or a design and build contractor), the ACoP (paragraphs 115–118) makes it clear that in CDM the term designer has a broad meaning, including:

- architects, civil and structural engineers, building surveyors, landscape architects, other consultants, manufacturers and design practices (of whatever discipline) contributing to, or having overall responsibility for, any part of the design, for example drainage engineers designing the drainage for a new development
- anyone who specifies or alters a design, or who specifies the use of a particular method of work or material, such as a design manager, quantity surveyor who insists on specific material or a client who stipulates a particular layout for a new building
- building service designers, engineering practices or others designing plant which forms part of the permanent structure (including lifts, heating, ventilation and electrical systems), for example a specialist provider of permanent fire extinguishing installations
- those purchasing materials where the choice has been left open, for example those purchasing building blocks and so deciding the weights that bricklayers must handle
- contractors carrying out design work as part of their contribution to a project, such as an engineering contractor providing design, procurement and construction management services
- temporary works engineers, including those designing auxiliary structures, such as formwork, formwork, falsework, façade retention schemes, scaffolding, and sheet piling
- interior designers, including shop-fitters who also develop the design
- heritage organisations who specify how work is to be done in detail, for example providing detailed requirements to stabilise existing structures
- those determining how buildings and structures are altered, eg during refurbishment, where this has the potential for partial or complete collapse.

Local authority or government officials may provide advice relating to designs and relevant statutory requirements, eg the Building Regulations, but this does not make them designers. This is because these are legal requirements where the designer has no choice in respect of compliance. Any such requirements should be treated as "design constraints" in the usual way. However, if the statutory bodies require that particular features which are not statutory requirements are included or excluded (eg stipulating the use of hazardous substances for cleaning or the absence of edge protection on flat roofs), then they are designers and must ensure that they comply with CDM2007.

Manufacturers supplying standardised products that can be used in any project are not designers under CDM2007, although they may have duties under supply legislation. The person who selects the product is a designer and must take account of health and safety issues arising from its use. If a product is purpose-made for a project, the person who prepares the specification is a designer under CDM2007, and so is the manufacturer who develops the detailed design.

Nearly all participants in a project could be designers, whether it be a client specifying a type of construction, or a subcontractor deciding how to work and designing a method of lifting and slinging.

The guidance provided in this report is for ALL designers. Note that designers are required to work as a team, assisted by the CDM coordinator. Decisions that are not in the control of one designer, due to the contractual framework, will be in the control of another designer. Each project will be different and it is therefore not appropriate for CDM2007 to set out exactly how the various designers on a project will interact. As the design progresses, designers will need to take account of decisions already made and information provided by others. They need to raise questions where necessary and make further decisions using their own expertise. Examples of areas of design that require careful coordination include:

❑ all interfaces between elements, particularly where there is a degree of interaction

❑ interfaces between permanent works and temporary works

❑ works that will be left in a temporary condition while other work continues.

## 1.4.3      Designers' duties

Designers' duties under CDM are contained in Regulations 11 and 18 and amplified in the ACoP paragraphs 109–145. All designers should read this guidance and become familiar with it.

Website <www.citb-constructionskills.co.uk/CDM> also gives guidance.

Designers must:

❑ ensure that their clients are aware of their duties under CDM and that (for notifiable projects) the correct steps have been taken (appointment of CDM coordinator, notification of HSE)

❑ ensure that they are competent and adequately resourced to address the H&S issues in their design work

❑ seek to eliminate hazards and reduce risks in their design

❑ cooperate and coordinate their work with the CDM coordinator and other designers

❑ provide information about significant residual risks, both before construction  as pre-construction information and  for the future in the health and safety file.

## 1.4.4      Information from clients

Designers should note that a client is required (Reg 10) to provide the CDM coordinator/designers with information that he could reasonably be expected to obtain, which will be relevant to the management of hazards and risks. This requirement may assist in persuading a reluctant client to commission surveys (in conjunction with an explanation of the benefits such work will bring to the project).

## 1.4.5      Designers' management of hazards and risks

CDM2007 requires (Regulation 11) that the designer shall, so far as is reasonably practicable, avoid foreseeable risks to people by eliminating hazards which give rise to risks and reducing risks from any remaining hazards, giving priority to collective measures (ie separating people from the hazard rather than providing PPE).

The duty is explained further in ACoP paragraphs 124–128:

"Designers have to weigh many factors as they prepare their designs. Health and safety considerations have to be weighed alongside other considerations, including cost, fitness for purpose, aesthetics, buildability, maintainability and environmental impact. CDM2007 allows designers to take due account of other relevant design considerations. The Regulations do not prescribe design outcomes, but they do require designers to weigh the various factors and reach reasoned, professional decisions.

**Designers are required to avoid foreseeable risks "so far as is reasonably practicable, taking account of other relevant design considerations". The greater the risk, the greater the weight that must be given to eliminating or reducing it.** Of course designers are not expected to consider or address risks which cannot be foreseen, and The regulations do not require zero risk designs because this is simply impossible. However, designers must not produce designs that cannot be constructed, maintained, used or demolished in reasonable safety.

Designers should critically assess their design proposals at an early stage, and then throughout the design process, to ensure that health and safety issues are identified, integrated into the overall design process and addressed as they go along. It is pointless to complete the design first, then try to address the risks which the design has introduced. By then, all of the key decisions are likely to have been taken and no one will be willing to make any changes because of the time and cost involved.

The first thing that designers need to do is eliminate hazards (things with a potential to cause harm) from their designs so far as is reasonably practicable, taking account of other design considerations. Examples would be to design out things like fragile roofing materials or products; eliminating rooflights from areas where roof access is needed; positioning plant which needs regular maintenance at ground level so there is no need for work at height or providing permanent safe access for work at height. Eliminating hazards removes the associated risk, and is therefore the best option and should always be the first choice.

It is not always reasonably practicable to eliminate hazards, and where this is the case consideration should be given to incorporating design solutions which reduce the overall risk to an acceptable level. This can be done by reducing the:

❏    likelihood of harm (injury or adverse health effect)

❏    potential severity of the harm

❏    number of people exposed to the harm

❏    frequency or duration of exposure to harm".

Limitations to the designers' duties are specifically covered in the ACoP paragraph 143:

"Under CDM, designers do not have to:

❏    take into account or provide information about unforeseeable hazards and risks

❏    design for possible future uses of structures that cannot reasonably be anticipated from their design brief

❏    specify construction methods, except where the design assumes or requires a particular construction or erection sequence, or where a competent contractor might need such information

❏    exercise any health and safety management function over contractors or others; or worry about trivial risks".

### 1.4.6    Hazard Elimination and Risk Reduction (HERR) by Designers

Designers need to examine ways in which hazards can be avoided or mitigated or, if neither is possible, designed for so that the level of risk is acceptable (given proper controls), applying the principles of prevention and protection. This process follows the requirements of the Regulations: *Hazard Elimination* and then *Risk Reduction* (HERR).

### 1.4.7    Designers' contribution to risk control

Risk control measures should preferably be collective rather than personal. In descending order of effectiveness, the hierarchy of risk control involves:

❏ changes that eliminate a hazard

❏ substitution of a less hazardous design feature

❏ enclosure – isolation, barriers, guarding or segregation, all of which are designed to separate people from the hazard

❏ reduced exposure – changes that reduce the time individuals are exposed to a risk, or the number of people exposed

❏ safe systems of work, together with suitable training and supervision

❏ written procedures, and the provision of information, instruction, warnings, signs and/or labels

❏ use of personal protective equipment (PPE).

Failure by designers to address a hazard may mean that contractors have to adopt less effective measures such as the use of PPE. *The designers' contribution to risk control therefore lies primarily in the scenario they set for the contractors.* Designers select the risks that contractors must manage and the provision of information about residual risk (although necessary, see below) is of importance only once the key design decisions that affect risk have been made.

## 1.4.8 Provision of information by designers

Designers have always provided information for construction, and under CDM2007 they need also to provide information for the health and safety file to guide and inform those responsible for future work (cleaning, maintaining, repairing, modifying, adapting and demolishing) on the structure. The ACoP (paragraph 131–133) states:

"Designers must provide information that other project team members are likely to need to identify and manage the remaining risks. **This should be project specific, and concentrate on significant risks which may not be obvious to those who use the design.** For example, providing generic risk information about the prevention of falls is pointless, because competent contractors will already know what needs to be done, but if the design gives rise to a specific and unusual fall risk which may not be obvious to contractors, designers should provide information about this risk.

Designers also need to provide information about aspects of the design that could create significant risks during future construction work or maintenance. If in doubt about the level of information needed, the best way to find out is to ask those who will use it.

Significant risks are not necessarily those that involve the greatest risks, but those, including health risks that are:

❑ not likely to be obvious to a competent contractor or other designers; unusual; or

❑ likely to be difficult to manage effectively".

The ACoP (paragraph 134) notes that the information must be "brief, clear, precise and in a form suitable for the users", for example by:

❑ notes on drawings (the best solution in most cases where the information is not long or complicated)

❑ supporting documents if necessary, referenced from the notes on the drawings

❑ suggested construction sequences showing how the design could be erected safely, where this is not obvious.

## 1.4.9          Issues of concern – questions and answers

These are commonly asked questions relating to designers' duties under CDM.

**1 Q** To what lengths do designers need to go in considering hazard and risk and providing guidance for construction work?

**A** Guidance is given in the ACoP (see Section 1.4.8 above). A competent designer has to be prepared to take a view on what is reasonable in the circumstances, all things being considered, at that time. Properly informed professional judgements need to be made. What will not be acceptable is a failure to consider hazards.

**2 Q** How does a designer decide whether to mention the need for specific controls?

**A** This will be when:

the client (reasonably) wishes a specific approach to be adopted, or the design requires specific precautions

or

a safe method of work has already been approved by a competent body.

**3 Q** How does a designer decide which risks need to be pointed out to contractors?

**A** This should be when a significant risk might not be recognised by a competent contractor or is of an unusual nature such that a designer is bound to draw it to the contractors' attention and suggest how it might be handled.

**4 Q** When considering how far to go in documenting project risks, does the likely type of contracting organisation need to be taken into account?

**A** This is a matter of judgement for designers based on what is known at the time, bearing in mind that they should be able to rely upon the appointment of competent contractors. A designer should identify to the person appointing a contractor if the design requires a contractor to have special skills or competencies beyond the norm for the type of project. Once the contractor has been appointed, the best way forward is to agree with them the information that they need.

**5 Q** Can information be shown on a number of documents as well as in the pre-construction information and does it need to be duplicated?

**A** Specific concerns should be mentioned in the pre-construction information. If they are important, experience shows that they will be more likely to be acted on if shown on the drawings or referenced from the drawings. Information on drawings is most likely to be seen by the individuals directly engaged in and managing the work on site.

**6 Q** Are control measures recommended by designers binding upon the contractors?

**A** Not unless it is written into the contract.

**7 Q** How can a designer decide on levels of risk and balance options?

**A** Decisions must be based on knowledge and experience. Advice from colleagues or experts should be sought if there is uncertainty on a particular point. Contractors may also be able to advise the designer on the relative health and safety merits of different design options. Note that designers should not agonise between options that will present similar levels of risk, but concentrate on those that could substantially reduce it, eg provision of a parapet rather than examining a steel/concrete option.

**8 Q** Do the health and safety aspirations of a client affect decisions?

**A** If a client wishes to aim for a higher standard of health and safety than would normally be required for basic legal compliance, this may affect decision-making and the site rules in pre-construction information. The client's requirements in this respect should be made plain at an early stage. The basic requirements of CDM will not be affected.

**9 Q** Does quality assurance (QA) play a role in Hazard Elimination and Risk Reduction (HERR) by designers?

**A** This is a business decision. However, risk management is fundamental to CDM and QA may be an appropriate management tool to monitor whether it is being carried out systematically and to demonstrate that the business is complying with statutory duties and company policies and procedures.

**10 Q** How do contractors' risk assessments relate to Hazard Elimination and Risk Reduction (HERR) by designers?

**A** Hazard Elimination and Risk Reduction (HERR) is used by designers to identify and assess hazards and to help them make decisions about design options. Contractors use risk assessment to develop a safe system of work that takes account of information in the pre-construction information and all project circumstances.

**11 Q** If the project is at an early stage (eg bidding for grants, obtaining estimates) or if no CDM coordinator is appointed by the time a designer is making decisions, is a designer relieved of his duties under Regulation 11?

**A** No. Regulation 11 duties are not dependent on the appointment of a CDM coordinator. However, note that a designer should not be making binding H&S related decisions if a CDM coordinator should have been appointed, only "initial design work" is permitted (see Reg 18 and ACoP paragraph 139). The designer has a duty to ensure (Regulation 11 (1)) that the client is aware when he should be appointing a CDM coordinator under CDM; if he fails to act, designers should remind him in writing if there is a risk that design could be seen as progressing beyond "initial design work" and pointing out the benefits of appointing the CDM coordinator. Action in the face of a blatant refusal to appoint when required by CDM2007 is difficult to recommend, being a commercial matter but the law under CDM2007 is clear.

## 1.4.10     Getting help

The HSE runs a helpline called 'Infoline', tel 0845 345 0055 fax 0845 408 9566 or email hse.infoline@natbrit.com and you can also visit their website <www.hse.gov.uk>.

## 1.5     HOW TO USE THIS GUIDANCE

The construction work sectors have been organised into five groups (A to E), each of which addresses a major area of construction work. Within each group the sectors are referenced numerically. The arrangement of the groups has been organised to reflect the order of construction where possible.

Each of the 39 construction work sectors is referenced as <Group letter><Work sector number> For example:

Deep basements and shafts is referenced as B2 (Group B, Work sector 2 in this group).

This referencing system is used for the internal cross-references between work sectors, principally in the "Related Issues" section.

In some instances sectors are intended to be read in conjunction with others, eg C1 (General concrete) should be read alongside any of the more specific concrete topics (C2, C3 or C4).

A detailed description of the way in which the sectors are arranged is given in Chapter 2.

## 1.6     FLOWCHART OF HAZARD ANALYSIS

Designers can follow a logical process to deal with the hazards that have been identified, either as typical generic hazards or as project specific. The outcome of this process will depend on the nature of the hazards and the limits of the project that is being considered. Figure 1.1 illustrates the process as a flowchart, starting with the identification of the hazards and concluding with the significant residual risks.

The three elements of Figure 1.1 are described below.

1   The design process is divided into three stages (concept, scheme and detail). Each design stage will address different issues, but typically the nature of issues will move from the general to the particular as the design is refined.

2   Once hazards have been identified, the CDM process is split into the three approaches (avoid, reduce, control) and each of these methods of solution is considered in turn. For example, reduction measures may be considered only if a hazard cannot reasonably be avoided.

3   The end of the hazard consideration in design process is the consideration of the residual risks that remain in the design. Those that are judged to be significant or unusual in the context of the project need to be identified. Information on these risks may need to be provided to those who need it

in order that appropriate action can be taken by the contractor, for construction, or the client (and others) for future work. This is considered further in Chapter 3.

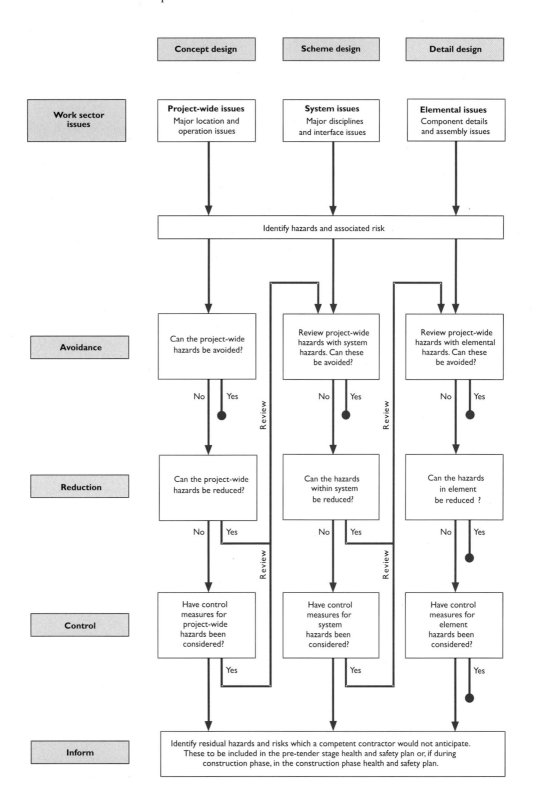

**Figure 1.1**   *Flowchart of hazard analysis*

This process of analysing and dealing with hazards is considered in the construction work sectors under the headings of "Hazard Consideration in Design" and "Examples". The "Hazard Consideration in Design" section within each sector assumes a parallel series of operations to analyse the various risks arising from the intended construction. These then determine the degree of effort designers should apply to eliminating or reducing the hazards and then informing others so that they can control them. This total process is referred to as ERIC (Eliminate, Reduce, Inform, Control).

## 1.7 GENERIC ISSUES

### 1.7.1 Introduction

The identification and consideration of health and safety hazards by construction work sector must be set within the wider context. This section looks at three such issues:

- common types of accident
- major health hazards
- planning and sequencing of construction.

There may be other issues that need to be considered on each particular project and designers should consider them in conjunction with the hazards related to construction work sectors.

### 1.7.2 Common types of accident

The main causes of injury in construction work are set out in Table 1.3. They happen in many different construction work sectors. It is essential for designers to have an appreciation of the part that they can play by eliminating the hazards and reducing the risks involved. Examples of preventative action are also shown in Table 1.3. It is important to understand that there are many designers involved in projects, including people who specify the materials to be used. Each needs to play their part, even though they cannot each address all of the issues.

**Table 1.3**    *Issues relating to types of accident*

| Risk | Examples of causes | Examples of preventive action |
|---|---|---|
| Falls from height | Fall from a flat roof<br><br>Fall through fragile roof/skylight<br><br>Fall from ladder | Design in parapet or barrier<br>Do not specify fragile materials<br><br>Design out the need for ladders during construction, cleaning and maintenance operations eg:<br>● sequence work to allow permanent stairways to be used during construction<br>● specify/sequence work to provide hard standing for mobile access equipment<br>● design windows to be cleaned from the inside<br>● specify materials that don't need routine painting or design in safe access for maintenance<br>● consider prefabrication so that sub-assemblies can be erected at ground level and then safely lifted into place<br>Design in permanent access equipment eg:<br>● rails for cradles/gantries<br>● anchorages for fall arrest equipment and rope access equipment |
| Trench collapse | Poor ground conditions | Ensure that there is adequate information about ground conditions and ground water<br>Seek to avoid deep excavation in poor conditions |
| Struck by moving vehicle | Poor site layout | Design site to:<br>● provide safe access and egress onto public roads<br>● ensure there is adequate space for plant and equipment to operate safely |
| Electric shock or burn | Contact with overhead or underground cables | Provide accurate information on all cables<br>Arrange for service diversions ahead of main works<br>Position structures to minimise risks from:<br>● buried services<br>● overhead cables |
| Collapse of structure during erection | Incorrect sequence of assembly leading to temporary instability | Suggest sequence of erection<br>Design in bracing to ensure stability during erection |

## 1.7.3    Major health hazards

Many more construction workers suffer serious health problems due to their work than serious accidents. Many of these health hazards can be avoided at the design stage. Table 1.4 gives some examples.

**Table 1.4**    *Issues relating to types of health hazard*

| Health problem | Typical causes | Preventative action |
| --- | --- | --- |
| Skeletal/muscular disorders | Laying heavy concrete blocks | Specify light blocks (n/e 20 kg) |
| | Laying kerb stones | Specify light block kerbs or extruded kerbs/ heavy sections that can only be lifted mechanically |
| | Needing to lift in an awkward way eg needing to twist and turn, particularly repeatedly | Design for ease of access eg avoiding need for awkward postures or twisting in plant rooms |
| Hand/arm vibration syndrome (HAVS) | Scabbling | Specify surface finishes that do not require scabbling |
| | Hand tunnelling | Minimise hand tunnelling eg specify size that will accommodate machinery |
| | Breaking out pile heads | Design piles so that mechanical pile head removal is possible; specify method |
| Dermatitis | Allergic reaction due to contact with wet cement | Design to use bulk supply pumped into position to minimise skin contact |
| | | Ensure that good welfare facilities are specified |
| | | Specify low chrome cement if skin contact is likely |
| Noise-induced hearing loss | Noisy machinery/ processes | Avoid the need for noisy processes such as mechanical breaking |
| Asbestosis, mesothelioma | Exposure to asbestos dust | Ensure that site has been surveyed to identify/locate any asbestos |
| Solvent exposure | Specification of solvent-based adhesives for large surfaces or in confined spaces | Specify adhesives with non-volatile solvents eg water-based |

Designers need to be aware of health hazards; guidance is provided in the *Site health handbook*, CIRIA publication C629. This is an area where new information and understanding often becomes available and designers will need to keep up-to-date through CPD activity.

### 1.7.4 Hazard Identification

A list of hazards is provided below to assist in appreciating risks. A list of this type can never be complete.

| | |
|---|---|
| falls | polluted, contaminated access |
| plant movement | struck by mobile plant |
| collapse | static machinery |
| services | electrical shock/fire/explosion |
| impact | impact |
| health hazards | crushing |
| collapse of excavation | poor visibility |
| flooding/fire/explosion | buried/crushed/trapped |
| services/electrocution | plant and machinery intrusive occurrences |
| falling from height | ground effects/movements |
| noise/vibration/dust | inundation |
| inadequate working space | plant instability |
| inadequate working platform | working environment |
| working environment | structural instability |
| inadequate access | fumes/heat |
| access to height/depth | irritants |
| manoeuvring vehicles | crushing |
| lifting, lowering loads | discarded syringes and sharps |
| handling | lasers |
| untidy, unsafe site | asbestos |
| radiation | |

### 1.7.5 Planning and sequencing of construction

At concept stage, the designers of a project can do a great deal to avoid and reduce significant hazards.

One important factor is the manner in which the site is laid out; is there room for the site establishment including materials storage and can safe delivery be made? These issues will also affected by the decisions made about the form of construction, eg the amount of on-site work which requires materials to be stored, mixed etc.

Another technique used to achieve safer construction is to alter the way the construction is planned, including the sequence of construction that is assumed. This is a powerful tool, but it requires wide understanding of the construction process and of the options that are feasible.

**Examples**

❑ Designers can reduce the potential for health problems arising from manual handling by producing a scheme that encourages mechanical lifting during maintenance operations and places a limit on the weights of objects to be handled manually. *These measures will not only improve the long-term health of operatives but should also improve productivity.*

❏ Designers can reduce the need to work at height when erecting a steel frame by designing the steelwork in modular sections, which can be pre-fabricated at ground level and sequentially lifted into place. This does not eliminate working at height entirely but should reduce it significantly. The safety of those who do have to work at height can further be enhanced if an adequately strong ground slab is installed before the steel frame so as to provide a stable, flat working surface from which mobile elevating work platforms can be used for bolting up. This is much safer than using ladder access and quicker than scaffolding. In addition, edge protection can be provided for in the design of the permanent works so that it is easy to install; where appropriate, it may be lifted into place as the works are erected. All of these measures have been found to improve productivity and speed on site.

Although designers are not expected (for normal structures) to specify particular construction methods or sequences, they will be expected to have considered possible alternatives when the hazards are being identified. If the assumptions of construction method and sequence become inextricably woven into the design, such that there is only one reasonable choice, then this will have to be made known.

Alternative methods and sequences will need to be considered to ensure that the appropriate choice is made. This will include factors other than health and safety and the final choice will reflect that health and safety is not expected to be pursued at any cost, rather that decisions have to be sensible and reasonable and balanced with other design decisions.

Table 1.5 demonstrates how options may be compared in a simple, effective manner, assisting decision-making.

**Table 1.5**    *Example of the assessment of alternative methods and sequences of construction*

| Consideration | Option 1 – Assembly *in situ* | Option 2 – Pre-assembly and lift into place |
|---|---|---|
| Health and safety | Operatives working at height, risk of people falling, risk of falling objects, risk of lifting many individual items | Fewer operatives working at height, risks from manipulating large modules, quicker site operation means shorter exposure times |
| Quality | Variable quality | Better opportunities for quality control |
| Programme | Assembly *in-situ* slower than prefabricating | Quicker than assembling *in-situ* in terms of site work. Pre-assembly can be elsewhere on site or remote. Requires longer lead time |
| Price | Usually little difference in cost of materials and components. Pre-assembly possibly more expensive in total manpower/double handling, eg needs larger crane, but should be more predictable out-turn price. | |
| Performance | In this instance, it is judged that there is no material difference in eventual performance of the structure arising from the choice of one construction method or another. | |

Note that comparisons will not always be necessary; the ACoP (paragraph 129) states:

"The amount of effort put in to eliminating hazards and reducing risks should depend on the degree of risk. There is little point in spending a lot of money, time and trouble on low risk issues. There is also little to be gained by detailed comparison of construction techniques that present similar risks, for example whether to specify a steel frame or concrete portal building. The focus should be on issues that are known to have the potential to cause significant harm, and where there are known solutions that reduce the risks to everyone exposed".

# 2      Construction work sector guidance

## 2.1    CONSTRUCTION WORK SECTOR GROUPS

The construction work sectors in this report are divided into five groups, relating to main stages of construction work, as follows:

**Group A**   General planning

**Group B**   Excavation and foundations

**Group C**   Primary structure

**Group D**   Building elements and building services

**Group E**   Civil engineering

Within these groups, each of the 39 sectors is presented in a standard format over four pages. Once readers are familiar with the layout and arrangement of the guidance material, it is expected that individual sectors will be referred to on a case-by-case basis and the structure of the guidance has been designed with this in mind. However, it is vital that users have read and understood the introduction to the report and also have access to the list of general reference material contained in Chapter 4 of the report.

## 2.2    THE CONTENT OF EACH CONSTRUCTION WORK SECTOR

Each of the construction work sectors is arranged over four pages, with a common structure of headings and subdivision of the information presented.

Table 2.1 indicates what each part of the common structure of the construction work sector guidance contains. In order to get maximum benefit from the guidance, readers must know where particular information is contained within each sector.

> Manual handling is a hazard potentially applicable to all construction processes. It has not been repeated in each section but must always be borne in mind.

**Table 2.1**     *Description of contents of each work sector*

| Page | Heading used | Contents |
|---|---|---|
| First | Scope | This describes what the work sector covers, either as a formal definition or as examples in bullet point form. |
| | Exclusions | This describes what is not included in the scope of the work sector, usually items that have been considered too specialist. |
| | Major hazards | These are hazards that will be most likely to arise when this work sector is included in a construction project; a maximum of six are given to concentrate on the major issues. |
| Second | Specific hazard Identification | This section gives typical issues that may arise, depending on the nature of the project the designer is undertaking, to add to those identified as major hazards. There are examples of specific questions, headed *Possible key considerations*. These are included to stimulate lateral thought, as it is impossible for any guidance of this kind to cover all possible eventualities. This list works in conjunction with the prompts. |
| | Prompts | This gives a list of general issues that may well influence how the key considerations are addressed. The list is NOT exhaustive and each prompt should be considered against each consideration. |
| | Hazard consideration in design | This section considers the issues that might arise at different stages of the design process (concept, scheme and detail), ranging from strategic questions at concept stage to specific issues at later stages. This section also presents some possible design options, which could allow the designer to avoid or reduce health and safety hazards. The design options are a starting point and must not be considered as a complete list. |
| Third | Examples of risk mitigation (methods of solution) | This sub-section considers typical issues, showing how these generate different responses, according to whether the hazard can be avoided or only reduced, or whether control measures are required as a last resort. |
| | Examples of risk mitigation (issues addressed at different stages) | This sub-section presents two typical projects to illustrate how a particular issue an be addressed in different ways as the design progresses from concept to detail stage. |
| Fourth | Related issues | This section identifies other work sectors within the report that have an impact on, or are affected by, the work sector in question. Work sectors are referenced by their letter and number – see Section 1.5. |
| | References for further guidance | This gives titles of other published guidance, arranged as primary, secondary and background references. General references that apply to the report as a whole are given in Chapter 4. The classification of a work sector in the Common Arrangement of Work Sectors, Civil Engineering Work Sectors and CI/SfB systems is also given where appropriate. |

# Group A – General planning
## 1 – Surrounding environment

Read the Introduction before using the following guidelines

## Scope

- Infrastructure – roads, railways, waterways, airport – load, length, width, height requirements.
- Adjacent environment – residential, commercial, industrial, conservation, leisure, civil.
- Transportation – plant, materials, personnel, to/from site, emergency facilities
- Occupation and activities of existing environment.
- Working procedures in an occupied building, etc.
- Topography – mining, lakes, rivers, quarries, caves, reservoirs, tidal areas.
- Adjacent structures and services – tall structures, basements, foundations, pipes, overhead cables, road, rail.
- Air rights (oversailing), railway rights, navigation rights.
- Site access, availability – parking, storage, road closures, low bridges, special access for surveys to railways, rivers, etc.
- Security exclusion of public from sites.

## Exclusions

- Special types of neighbourhood (eg nuclear installations, defence establishments).

## Major hazards

Refer to the Introduction for details of accident types and health risks

**Falls**
Work area perimeter security, preventing unauthorised access to active work areas.

**Plant movement**
Onto and off site plant and transportation loads/access/routes/noise.

**Collapse**
Working adjacent to previous excavations or existing/adjacent structures, old mine workings.

**Services**
Existing services, overhead, underground, buried, unknown, on-site, in buildings.

**Impact**
Plant lifting/over-sailing above local sensitive areas, shopping areas, schools, pavements, roads.

**Health hazards**
Dust, emissions from adjacent premises, dumps, sewers, ground seepage. Contaminated land.

GENERAL PLANNING — A1

EXCAVATIONS AND FOUNDATIONS — B

PRIMARY STRUCTURE — C

BUILDING ELEMENTS AND BUILDING SERVICES — D

CIVIL ENGINEERING — E

# A1 Group A – General planning
## 1 – Surrounding environment

B EXCAVATIONS AND FOUNDATIONS

C PRIMARY STRUCTURE

D BUILDING ELEMENTS AND BUILDING SERVICES

E CIVIL ENGINEERING

## Specific hazard identification

**Possible key considerations:**

- **Surroundings** – What are the health hazards in the proximity (airborne, buried, industrial, commercial liquid/dust/solid, etc)?

- **Infrastructure** – Where is the review of the infrastructure to ensure that it is able safely to support site traffic (load, frequency, duration, etc)?

- **Project** – What health hazards will the project construction place on the surrounding environment?

- **Methods** – Where have those situations that require method statements or controls been identified?

- **Information** – How will information be obtained from the client?

- **Services** – What hazards exist from surroundings (buried services, overhead cables, etc)?

- **Any others?**

## Prompts

- Road infrastructure
- Rail/air/water transportation
- Services in site proximity
- Sequence of construction
- Ground conditions
- Sensitive areas/noise, vibration
- Offsite deposit
- Offsite storage
- Fire
- Emergency services

## Hazards consideration in design

| Stage | Considerations and issues | Possible design options to avoid or mitigate hazards identified from surrounding environment |
|---|---|---|
| Concept design | • Why build here?<br>• Infrastructure scope<br>• Neighbours assessed?<br>• Shift working<br>• Local climate<br>• Access routes for site<br>• Known contamination | • Reduce contaminated ground hazards by containment.<br>• Avoid open excavation to reduce hazards of adjacent contaminated ground.<br>• Consider if the area poses increased risks of fire, flood or other hazards to site.<br>• Ensure that local roads and infrastructure can carry the elements (as designed) without hazard to operatives/public. |
| Scheme design | • Adjacent structures<br>• Adjacent emissions<br>• Oversailing adjacent buildings/areas<br>• Pollutants<br>• Local transport<br>• Topography<br>• Sensitive areas | • Design to suit local conditions, eg avoid basements in flooded ground; avoid work at height in exposed areas.<br>• Use shafts and headings to avoid need for deep open trenches.<br>• Foundations to suit site ground conditions (eg sheet piling in loose ground).<br>• Avoid over-sailing adjacent property, fix windows from within building. |
| Detail design | • External services<br>• Existing structures<br>• Security of site working<br>• Vehicle movements<br>• Sequence restrictions<br>• Time restrictions | • If shift or extended sequence of work required, design for off-site fabrication, minimise site activities.<br>• For work in restricted areas, adapt the design (eg avoid brickwork in tidal excavations, use pre-cast elements – plastic or cast iron pipework).<br>• Design to avoid existing services rather than re-route them. |

# Group A – General planning
## 1 – Surrounding environment

## Examples of risk mitigation (methods of solution)

| ACTION | ISSUE: Local traffic congestion | Damage to adjacent buildings and services |
|---|---|---|
| **Avoidance**<br>Design to avoid identified hazards but beware of introducing others | Locate site access/egress away from local traffic. | Locate new foundations remote from adjacent buildings. Avoid locations with existing services. |
| **Reduction**<br>Design to reduce identified hazards but beware of increasing others | Re-route local traffic away from site. | Allow for an independent compatible foundation. Divert existing services routes. |
| **Control**<br>Design to provide acceptable safeguards for all remaining identified hazards | Control site traffic which is local to work activities. | |

## Examples of risk mitigation (issues addressed at different stages)

Old properties adjacent to the site are founded upon made-up ground. The basement of the new building is to cover part of the site and extends up to the adjacent party walls. The facade of the building on the site is to be retained, but is presently founded at a higher level than the proposed new building foundations.

| Concept design | Scheme design | Detail design |
|---|---|---|
| To reduce the risk of collapse of adjacent structures resulting from ground movement, the designer has redesigned the new basement. | Allow the new structure to provide support to the facade during construction, avoiding temporary supports. | The designer will outline the procedures for supporting the retained facade during construction. |

A new sewage treatment plant for a small town has been relocated, at feasibility study stage, due to surrounding ground conditions. However, the new location will require a longer route for the main sewer. The new sewer pipe has to pass through areas of existing services and has to withstand a high water table.

| Concept design | Scheme design | Detail design |
|---|---|---|
| Designers are seeking ways of reducing costs of the increased length of main sewer, mindful of health and safety. | A design review identifies opportunities to reduce hazards of trench excavation through zones of existing services, by review of detailed alignment. | Access chambers will be designed in pre-cast concrete to include details that will reduce site activities in continuously pumped excavations. |

**A1** GENERAL PLANNING

**B** EXCAVATIONS AND FOUNDATIONS

**C** PRIMARY STRUCTURE

**D** BUILDING ELEMENTS AND BUILDING SERVICES

**E** CIVIL ENGINEERING

## Related issues

References within this document

| References | Related issues |
|---|---|
| A2 | Site clearance activities will need to consider environment. |
| A3 | Site investigation may confirm significant surrounding influences. |
| A4 | Access onto the site is likely to be determined by surrounding environment. |
| A5 | Site layout will be affected by the surroundings and access requirements. |
| B1–B3 | Excavation planning needs to consider surroundings, underground, overhead services, etc. |
| B5–B7 | Foundations may undermine or load surroundings. |
| C1–C4 | Concrete materials brought to site in bulk. |
| C5–C6 | Structural steel may require special access to site. |
| C7 | Timber may be influenced by the surrounding environment. |
| C8 | Masonry materials will require regular access to site for deliveries. |
| D5 | Surface coatings/finishes may require special protection to prevent unsafe spreading during application. |
| D1 | External cladding will need access and off-loading facilities. |
| D6 | Cleaning buildings may oversail adjacent properties. |
| D7–D9 | Services will be influenced by demands from site. |
| E2 | Roads may affect access/egress limits to the site. |
| E3 | Railways may assist or constrain the site access. |

## References for further guidance

Primary general references and background information given in Section 4

### Primary

- CIRIA PR70 (1999) How much noise do you make? A guide to assessing and managing noise on construction sites
- CIRIA SP96 (1994) Environmental assessment – A guide to the identification, evaluation and mitigation of environmental issues in construction schemes
- HSE HSG66 Protection of workers and the general public during the development of contaminated land
- BRE IP 2/87 (1987) Fire and explosion hazards associated with the redevelopment of contaminated land
- HSE HSG151 Protecting the public – Your next move

### Secondary

- DTLR (2001) Safety at street works and road works: a code of practice

### Background

- CIRIA C650 (2005) Environmental good practice on site
  CIRIA C651 (2005) Environmental good practice pocket book
- CIRIA SP111 (1995) Remedial treatment of contaminated land Vol XI: Planning and management
- BS 10175 (2001) Identification of potentially contaminated land and its investigation: code of practice
- Cairney, T and Hobson, C M (1998) Contaminated land: problems and solutions. 2nd ed (Spon)

### Classification

**CAWS** Group A,     **CEWS** Class A,     **CI/SfB** Code (--)(H)

Read the Introduction before using the following guidelines

## Scope

- Earth moving – loading, transporting, placing.
- Tree-felling, mast/pole/post.
- Waste removal – safe, toxic, suitable transport, licensed tip.
- Excavation – clays, granular, rock material, contaminated ground.
- Water removal – fresh, salt, foul, brackish, contamination of water courses.
- Services – above/below ground, tunnels, pipes, wires, diversions, relocations.
- Structures – above/below ground, party walls.
- Demolition – brickwork, timber, concrete, steel, asbestos, lead-based paints, etc.
- Partial removal of materials – site clearance/demolition.
- Recycling of materials – temporary storage, crushing, sorting

## Exclusions

- Special conditions – unusual, unstable, (eg shallow mine workings).
- Radio-active areas.
- Below water – use of divers, dredging, etc.
- Buried explosives – mines, terrorist action.

## Major hazards

Refer to the Introduction for details of accident types and health risks

**Collapse of excavation**
Buried obstructions, underground voids, unexpectedly poor ground conditions, water table.

**Health hazards**
Toxic waste, decomposing materials causing gaseous emissions, asbestos, microbiological agents.

**Flooding/Fire/Explosion**
From underground or above ground services.

**Services/electrocution**
Underground services, overhead cables, fixed equipment on site.

**Falling from height**
Loose/unstable material, access, inadequate support.

**Noise/vibration/dust**
Breaking-up of building fabric with mechanical breakers, asbestos, silica.

A2 GENERAL PLANNING

B EXCAVATIONS AND FOUNDATIONS

C PRIMARY STRUCTURE

D BUILDING ELEMENTS AND BUILDING SERVICES

E CIVIL ENGINEERING

## Specific hazard identification

**Possible key considerations:**

- **Previous uses** – Where have previous uses of site been established?
- **Site survey** – When was a full site survey carried out?
- **Hazardous materials** – What are procedures to deal with hazardous materials?
- **Toxicity** – What is extent of hazardous materials' volume/toxicity, particularly asbestos?
- **Clearance** – Clearance causes dust hazards: prepare plans to define and contain it.
- **Unstable site** – Is the site unstable? Will clearance cause instability? Review any risks of flooding.
- **Demolition** – How are structures constructed and will it affect methods of demolition?
- **Handling** – What materials during clearance are hazardous to handle?
- **Services** – Identify existing above/below ground services and installations.
- **Any others?**

## Prompts

- Existing health and safety file
- Client information
- Site records/drawings
- Investigation results
- Fill source
- Site security
- Site access
- Sequence of working
- Structural records
- Plant routes
- Personnel routes
- Health
- Fire

## Hazards consideration in design

| Stage | Considerations and issues | Possible design options to avoid or mitigate hazards identified for site clearance |
|---|---|---|
| Concept design | • Location – why here?<br>• Bulk transport capability<br>• Hazardous materials<br>• Previous site use<br>• Flood prevention<br>• Demolition | • Ensure complete up-to-date description of existing site services.<br>• Build remote from major existing services.<br>• Avoid trees, rather than remove and replace. |
| Scheme design | • Phasing activities<br>• Transport plan<br>• Site contamination<br>• Surveys/records known<br>• Clearance methods<br>• Demolition method<br>• Elemental clearance<br>• Sequencing of work | • Seal contaminated ground on site, if possible, rather than excavate and replace with fill.<br>• Store and re-use material on site; avoid transportation off-site.<br>• Avoid existing services rather than protect them.<br>• Design service diversions to avoid/minimise site clearance.<br>• Design new foundation to avoid existing obstructions. |
| Detail design | • Stability of ground<br>• Stability of structures<br>• Clearance activities<br>• Demolition procedure<br>• Landscape profile | • Optimise site filling with excavated material (cut and fill).<br>• Use site demolition material as hard-core fill.<br>• Use driven piled foundations through contaminated ground, to minimise open excavation. |

## Examples of risk mitigation (methods of solution)

| ACTION \ ISSUE | Contaminated ground | Demolition of large house on new development |
|---|---|---|
| **Avoidance**<br>Design to avoid identified hazards but beware of introducing others | Proposed structures relocated, ground not disturbed. | Incorporate house into overall scheme with possible conversion to flats. |
| **Reduction**<br>Design to reduce identified hazards but beware of increasing others | Contaminated ground identified and sealed. | Highlight site constraints. |
| **Control**<br>Design to provide acceptable safeguards for all remaining identified hazards | Contaminated ground removed under controlled monitoring. | Recommend a sequence of demolition following survey. |

## Examples of risk mitigation (issues addressed at different stages)

A small enabling works contract is to be let for site clearance prior to the main contract. The site is adjacent to a main road which is particularly busy during rush hours. There are also colleges and schools in the area, so the pavements are usually crowded. The site clearance requires some ground works excavation and hardstanding. The site is to be fenced and made secure.

| Concept design | Scheme design | Detail design |
|---|---|---|
| Careful consideration will be given to site layout and the surrounding environment, in order to reduce number of traffic movements. | Location of the site entrance and access roads will be planned to reduce hazards of site transport activities accessing and leaving the site. | The site entrance is designed to allow measures to be implemented to control site traffic across the pavement access. |

Several properties dating from the late 19th century are to be demolished to allow for a new development. There are no construction drawings for the largest building on the site and the method of construction for this building will require to be established before demolition planning can take place. The building has been modified on several occasions since it was originally built.

| Concept design | Scheme design | Detail design |
|---|---|---|
| The existing building will be surveyed in order to identify the structural systems and key demolition issues. | Part of the building is load-bearing brickwork with pre-stressed concrete slabs and beams. Information to be included in the pre-tender stage H&S Plan, to alert tendering contractors to demolition hazards. | To control site hazards of sudden failure, pre-stressed beams and slabs to be removed and broken up in a controlled condition at ground level. This is considered less hazardous than propping all the elements and breaking them up at height. |

**A2** GENERAL PLANNING

**B** EXCAVATIONS AND FOUNDATIONS

**C** PRIMARY STRUCTURE

**D** BUILDING ELEMENTS AND BUILDING SERVICES

**E** CIVIL ENGINEERING

## Related issues

References within this document

| References | Related issues |
| --- | --- |
| A4 | Access onto/within the site to be kept clear and safe during site clearance. |
| A5 | Site layout plays an important part in site clearance and following activities. |
| A1 | Surrounding environment will need to be protected from the hazards of site clearance and demolition. |
| A3 | Site investigation will be early and may need to interface with site clearance. |
| B1 | General excavation could be part of or follow site clearance. |
| B2 | Deep basement excavation could be required to interface with site clearance. |
| B3 | Trenches for foundations/services for early enabling works. |
| B4 | Retaining wall excavation may interface with site clearance. |
| B5 | Ground stabilization may be needed before or after site clearance activities. |
| B6 | Piling foundations will interface with site clearance and may form part of it. |
| B7 | Foundation underpinning before or after site clearance. |
| E1 | Small civil engineering works likely before or after site clearance . |
| E2 | Work adjacent to roads needs to be considered together with all other public areas. |
| E3 | Work adjacent to railways will have procedural implications on clearance and demolition. |

## References for further guidance

Primary general references and background information given in Section 4

### Primary

- HSE HSG66 Protection of workers and the general public during the redevelopment of contaminated land
- HSE INDG258 Safe work in confined spaces
- HSE GS29 Parts 1 to 4 Health and safety in demolition work
- CIRIA SP78 (1991) Building on derelict land
- DoT, Interdepartmental Committee on the Redevelopment of Contaminated Land (ICRCL) Guidance Note 17/78 Notes on the development and after-use of landfill sites 1990

### Secondary

- CIRIA SP38 (1985) The use of screens to reduce noise from sites
- CIRIA R97 (1992) Trenching practice
- HSE MDHS100 Surveying sampling and assessment of asbestos coating materials
- CIRIA C607 (2004) Design for deconstruction

### Background

- BS 6031:1981 Code of practice for earthworks
- BS 6187:2000 Code of practice for demolition
- Institute of Demolition Engineers Orchard W.R. Elements of Risk and Safety Management in Demolition and Dismantling Projects
- Institute of Demolition Engineers Seminar Proceedings Demolition and the CDM Regulations, 2001

### Classification

**CAWS** Group A&C, **CEWS** Class D,E,I,J,K,L,R,T,X&Y, **CI/SfB** Code (1-)(D2)

Read the Introduction before using the following guidelines

## Scope

- Structural surveys – including those in confined spaces.
- Building services surveys.
- Materials survey (eg asbestos, lead-based paint).
- Ground/soil sampling.
- Topographical/ground movement surveys.
- Rock coring.
- Boreholes/deep drilling at small diameter.
- Trial pits and excavations.
- Field testing – in-situ tests.
- Existing services location/inspection – pipes, cables, sewers.

## Exclusions

- Testing – eg underwater.
- Traffic surveys.
- Use of specialist equipment – towers, scaffolds, jetties etc.

## Major hazards

Refer to the Introduction for details of accident types and health risks

**Inadequate working space**
Width, height for identified situations, entrapment, awkward heavy lifting, manoeuvring.

**Inadequate working platform**
Capacity to support load/weight, slope instability, underground voids.

**Working environment**
Ventilation, illumination, hearing, tripping, collision, falling through openings or from edges.

**Excavation collapse**
Depth/dimensions for soil conditions, water table shoring, supervision, descent, falling, collapse, slip.

**Health hazards**
Noxious fumes, toxic, corrosive, explosive, microbiological, burial grounds.

**Services**
Excavation, drilling.
Sampling/testing.
Location of existing services.

GENERAL PLANNING **A 3**

EXCAVATIONS AND FOUNDATIONS **B**

PRIMARY STRUCTURE **C**

BUILDING ELEMENTS AND BUILDING SERVICES **D**

CIVIL ENGINEERING **E**

A3 GENERAL PLANNING

B EXCAVATIONS AND FOUNDATIONS

C PRIMARY STRUCTURE

D BUILDING ELEMENTS AND BUILDING SERVICES

E CIVIL ENGINEERING

## Specific hazard identification

**Possible key considerations:**

- **Safe working** – Provision for working at height or in confined spaces or in traffic (etc)?
- **Route** – Where are adequate provisions for access to investigation point?
- **Access** – Plan adequate room for access around investigation zone?
- **Stability** – Have you ensured that the site or working platform is stable?
- **Asbestos and other contaminants** – Is full information available?
- **Contamination** – How is the contamination to be treated?
- **Services** – Where have services been located/exposed/ disconnected?
- **Environment** – How will environmental control in confined spaces be done?
- **Equipment** – Where have you identified heavy equipment to be used?
- **Existing structures** – What effect will investigation have on existing structures and/or existing services?
- **What is the age and condition of buildings?**
- **Any others?**

## Prompts

- Access routes
- Services
- Desk study
- Sequence of investigation
- Work access
- Site hoardings
- Health
- Fire
- Method statements

## Hazards consideration in design

| Stage | Considerations and issues | Possible design options to avoid or mitigate hazards identified for site investigation |
|---|---|---|
| Concept design | • Location – why here?<br>• Previous use/surveys<br>• Existing features<br>• Access/exposure | • Check that sources of existing information will be able to provide relevant information.<br>• Consider the likely completeness and accuracy of available information and the practicality of obtaining an independent survey or investigation. |
| Scheme design | • Unknown features<br>• Scope of survey<br>• Stability of site<br>• Working environment<br>• Hazardous materials<br>• Existing conditions<br>• Survey equipment<br>• Contamination | • If weather has an influence on the intended investigation, check or define the preferred period of execution.<br>• Review whether the investigation team could be better informed or protected by a pre-investigation survey or cleansing operation. |
| Detail design | • Setting out probes<br>• Investigation access<br>• Existing services<br>• Temporary works<br>• Specific conditions | • Relate the distribution of boreholes, etc to the location and size of potential voids/obstructions but with respect to accessibility and potential buried obstructions.<br>• Highlight risks with the use of electricity in particular situations. |

# Group A – General planning
## 3 – Site investigation and remediation

## Examples of risk mitigation (methods of solution)

| ACTION / ISSUE | Structural behaviour | Site exploration |
|---|---|---|
| **Avoidance** — Design to avoid identified hazards but beware of introducing others | Previous structural drawings exist. | Boreholes samples and laboratory testing. |
| **Reduction** — Design to reduce identified hazards but beware of increasing others | Pre-demolition structural survey. | Trial pits sampling. |
| **Control** — Design to provide acceptable safeguards for all remaining identified hazards | Ensure technical demolition supervision. | In-situ field tests. |

## Examples of risk mitigation (issues addressed at different stages)

A soils site investigation is to be carried out. It is known that various live services cross the site. Measures will be required to be taken to avoid damaging live services and causing injury to operatives carrying out the site investigation.

| Concept design | Scheme design | Detail design |
|---|---|---|
| Soils investigation, where possible, will be set out to avoid areas of known live services. | Exploration points are required in areas of existing services. To reduce the hazard, starter pits will be used for boreholes in close proximity to live services. | To reduce the hazard of live services, arrange for isolation of existing services not required, before starting site investigation work. |

A group of buildings are to be extensively refurbished. Some drawings of the existing buildings are missing and existing services drawings are particularly incomplete. The services will be substantially replaced with a fully air-conditioned building.

| Concept design | Scheme design | Detail design |
|---|---|---|
| A site investigation will be carried out to set-out existing services and insulation, to identify hazards from services and possible asbestos insulation. | During the survey to locate existing services, extensive asbestos insulation was found. The concept design was amended to avoid this hazard. | Designer sets down control procedures for isolating existing services and removing hazardous insulation prior to refurbishment activities. |

A3 GENERAL PLANNING

B EXCAVATIONS AND FOUNDATIONS

C PRIMARY STRUCTURE

D BUILDING ELEMENTS AND BUILDING SERVICES

E CIVIL ENGINEERING

## Related issues

References within this document

| References | Related issues |
|---|---|
| A2 | Ground contamination will influence precautions required for spoil disposal |
| A2 | Demolition strategy to be incorporated into brief for site investigation. |
| A4 | Work in areas liable to flooding will generate special access requirements. |
| A4 | Work on slopes may create stability problems and will generate special access requirements. |
| A5 | Layout and structural capacity of existing buildings may influence feasibility and location of internal borings. |
| B1 | Reinstatement of boreholes and pits to be considered in the design of any future excavation or foundation work. |
| B5 | Shoring of trial pits will depend on stability of ground as assessed in the field. |

## References for further guidance

Primary general references and background information given in Section 4

### Primary

- The Electricity Association, Avoidance of danger from underground electricity cables
- British Gas, Precautions to be taken when working in the vicinity of underground gas pipes
- HSE HSG47 Avoiding danger from underground services
- HSE INDG258 Safe work in confined spaces
- HSE HSG66 Protection of workers and the general public during the development of contaminated land
- CIRIA SP73 (1991) Roles and responsibility in site investigation
- CIRIA SP 25 (1983) Site Investigation Manual
- CIRIA SP102–112 (various dates) Remedial treatment for contaminated land – Vols 2–12
- CIRIA C659 (2006) Assessing risks posed by hazardous gases to buildings

### Secondary

- CIRIA R97 (1992) Trenching practice
- HSE GS6 Avoidance of danger from overhead electric power lines

### Background

- BS 5930:1999 Code of Practice for Site Investigation
- Clayton C R I et al (1995) Site investigation (Blackwell)
- Institution of Civil Engineers (1993) Specification for ground investigation (Thomas Telford)

### Classification

**CAWS** Group D,     **CEWS** Class B,     **CI/SfB** Code (1-)(A3s)

Read the Introduction before using the following guidelines

## Scope

- Site perimeter – appropriate site access and security, boundary constraints.
- Site perimeter/building relationship – storage, handling and layout areas, welfare areas.
- Protection, illumination, visibility, ventilation, escape routes designed in.
- Building/structure, envelope, sequence of building operations.
- Emergency routes, compartmentation during construction, escape routes protection.
- Width, height, length, curvature, load – carrying capacity, overhead cables/services.
- Movement of personnel, vehicles, plant, materials.
- Site horizontal movement – roads, railways, waterways, footways, conveyors.
- Site vertical movement – stairs, ramps, shutes, hoists, cranes, pumps, cradles, lifts.

## Exclusions

- Specialist access – aerial lifts, helicopters, abseiling, etc.
- Unstable structures – bomb-blasted, fire-damaged, defective, partial failure, etc.
- Tunnels and shafts.
- Radio-active contaminated areas.

## Major hazards

Refer to the Introduction for details of accident types and health risks

GENERAL PLANNING   A4

EXCAVATIONS AND FOUNDATIONS   B

PRIMARY STRUCTURE   C

BUILDING ELEMENTS AND BUILDING SERVICES   D

CIVIL ENGINEERING   E

**Inadequate access**
Width, height for identified situations. Capacity to withstand load/weight. Overhead cables.

**Access to height/depth**
Height, falling, struck. Depth; entrapment, asphyxiation, drowning.

**Manoeuvring vehicles, plant and materials**
Turning reversing, clearance, height, width. Two-way traffic, lack of storage layout.

**Lifting, lowering loads**
Clearance, lifting, slewing, handling, visibility, site lines, capacity, oversailing public access areas.

**Working environment**
Noise, non-separation of plant and people, poor visibility.

**Polluted, contaminated access**
Poor ventilation, poor illumination, dust, damp, dirt.

# A4

## Group A – General planning
## 4 – Access (onto and within site)

A4

A
4
GENERAL PLANNING

B
EXCAVATIONS
AND FOUNDATIONS

C
PRIMARY STRUCTURE

D
BUILDING ELEMENTS
AND BUILDING SERVICES

E
CIVIL ENGINEERING

### Specific hazard identification

**Possible key considerations:**

- **Access** – Plan adequate provision for access at site perimeter?
- **Site traffic** – Where will site traffic cross a public road, pavement and/or existing services to gain access to the site?
- **Access zone** – Ensure there is adequate room for access around/over the construction zone within the site at all levels.
- **Sequence** – Where will access within the site have to change as construction progresses?
- **Constraints** – Does the client's on-going business affect the work area, eg supermarket, hotel, process plant?
- **Separation** – Set out separation of vehicles/plant and from operatives activities.
- **Interfaces** – Carefully identify vehicles/plant/operatives crossings/interfaces.
- **Lifting zone** – Where have you identified lifting zones (locate cranes/hoists)?
- **Site layout** – Where have you identified delivery, laydown and storage areas to reduce manual handling and allow for mechanical lifting appliances?
- **Any others?**

### Prompts

- Public – pedestrian, vehicular
- Plant and machinery routes
- Pedestrian routes
- Manual handling
- Mechanical lifting
- Movement of large units
- Existing services – divert?
- Overhead cables – divert?
- Lifting zones
- Restrictions, weight, size
- Emergency services
- Access routes
- Materials routes
- Storage areas
- Work areas
- Welfare areas
- Health issues
- Sequence of construction
- Fire
- Security
- Signage

### Hazards consideration in design

| Stage | Considerations and issues | Possible design options to avoid or mitigate hazards identified for access (onto and within site) |
|---|---|---|
| Concept design | • Location – why here? <br> • Main access, egress <br> • Building activities | • Traffic study to improve layout of site entrance and access. <br> • Ensure phased completion maintains construction access routes. <br> • Identify adequate site access to allow the design to be built safely. <br> • Design to maintain emergency access to site. |
| Scheme design | • Emergency services <br> • Site perimeter secure <br> • Footprint of structure/building <br> • Access within site and around building systems <br> • Within perimeter <br> • Movements in space between elements | • Design of permanent works to allow adequate temporary site access. <br> • Design to provide for safe access to repair and maintain the building. <br> • If access is conditional upon sequence, define the necessary sequence for safety throughout. <br> • Emergency – identify and display services isolation points. |
| Detail design | • Access in relation to site elements <br> • Access to each building element | • Consider the likely working space required for safe construction of the various elements. <br> • Consider the site work location (eg avoid site welding over/near public). <br> • Consider light, ventilation and time available for the site activity. <br> • In emergencies, workforce accessible to paramedics and stretchers. |

## Examples of risk mitigation (methods of solution)

| ACTION / ISSUE | Deliveries to city site building | Framed building construction |
|---|---|---|
| **Avoidance**<br>Design to avoid identified hazards but beware of introducing others | Design to allow lorries to unload within building footprint. | Design for permanent stairways to be installed as part of frame. |
| **Reduction**<br>Design to reduce identified hazards but beware of increasing others | Design components to be packaged to reduce unloading time in road. | Design fixings inside lift shafts to support temporary stairs. |
| **Control**<br>Design to provide acceptable safeguards for all remaining identified hazards | Highlight need to plan deliveries at off peak periods. | Highlight hazards involved when using ladders. |

## Examples of risk mitigation (issues addressed at different stages)

A city development site has very restricted access. The design team have agreed that special consideration will have to be given throughout the design to the particular difficulties of accessing this project during construction and subsequent maintenance.

| Concept design | Scheme design | Detail design |
|---|---|---|
| To avoid site access difficulties, elements to have overall envelope of not more than 10m length x 3m x 2m x 20 tonnes. | To reduce site access hazards of the large atrium roof spans, a review of the structural element option has identified steel roof trusses as the preferred option. | Detail design hazards will be avoided with a steel roof truss to be designed for final assembly at ground level on site and then lifted into position. |

A hospital has been planned to have the plant room for major plant at basement level.

| Concept design | Scheme design | Detail design |
|---|---|---|
| Provision will be made for 4 boilers in the plantroom at basement level. Only 3 boilers will be installed during construction, through temporary works access over the plantroom. | The design will allow for a dedicated access route for boiler maintenance, removal and installation of the 4th boiler. | Design load and space checks on dedicated plant access route to include boilers, trolleys, lifting beams and winch points. |

**A4** GENERAL PLANNING

**B** EXCAVATIONS AND FOUNDATIONS

**C** PRIMARY STRUCTURE

**D** BUILDING ELEMENTS AND BUILDING SERVICES

**E** CIVIL ENGINEERING

## Related issues

References within this document

| References | Related issues |
|---|---|
| A1 | Surrounding environment will have an influence on the way that the site is accessed. |
| A2 | Site clearance strategy to be incorporated into early phases of access planning of the site. |
| A5 | Site layout of temporary and permanent works will have a considerable influence on the access plan, ensure sealing (fire protection) during construction. |
| B1-B4 | Excavation may affect the phasing of access to the various work faces as well as the site perimeter. |
| B6 | Piling planning should maintain adequate access to the site. |
| C5,C6 | Structural steel erection will affect both horizontal and vertical movement, limiting access for other activities. |
| D1 | Cladding delivery, storage, lifting, positioning and fixing require detailed consideration of access routes. |
| D4 | Windows/glazing, because they are fragile require careful integration into the works sequence, perhaps with temporary dedicated access. |
| E2 | Permanent road construction will need to be considered when sequencing the temporary/permanent site access plan. |
| E4,E5 | Bridge construction/maintenance is likely to require specialised access to carry out the work. |
| E6 | Work over water will generate access requirements that are equally, if not more, demanding than land-based work. |

## References for further guidance

Primary general references and background information given in Section 4

### Primary

- CIRIA SP121 (1995) Temporary access to the workface: a handbook for young professionals
- HSE HSG47 Avoiding danger from underground services
- HSE INDG258 Safe work in confined spaces
- HSE GS6 Avoidance of danger from overhead electric power lines

### Secondary

- CIRIA C703 (2003) Crane stability on site.
- CIRIA C654 (2006) Tower crane stability
- HSE CIS5 (revised) Temporarily suspended access cradles and platforms

### Background

- CIRIA SP151 (2001) Site safety handbook

### Classification

**CAWS** Group A,     **CEWS** Class A,     **CI/SfB** Code (--)(A5)

Read the Introduction before using the following guidelines

## Scope

- Structure mass/site plan – restrictions imposed by adjacent buildings/land use.
- Site topography – alignment, stability, level, slope, terrain, groundwater.
- Site ergonomics – traffic routes, movements, personnel, plant, machinery, materials.
- Site entrances/exits – pedestrian, vehicular, site lines, site signage.
- Site security, prevention of flooding, interface with occupiers, other trades.
- Services, fuel storage – electricity, water oil, gas, overhead/underground.
- Plant layout/routes – tower cranes, mobiles/position, reach.
- Site accommodation – location of, and access to welfare, site storage layout.
- Emergency access/first aid – accommodation, facilities, staff.

## Exclusions

- Specialist areas
  - Nuclear installations
  - Floating facilities
  - Petro-chemical works
  - Quarries
  - Airfields (Active).

## Major hazards

Refer to the Introduction for details of accident types and health risks

**Struck by mobile plant**
Impact, crushing, slipping, falling, two way traffic, working cranes.

**Static machinery**
Inadequate protection and alerts to static machines operating.

**Electrical shock, fire, explosion**
Location of site services, temporary, permanent storage of flammable gases, liquids.

**Falling from height**
Falling from structure or falling into excavation.

**Impact, crushing**
Objects falling from height from insecure location, work overhead, delivery and storage, unstable structures.

**Poor visibility**
Layout of access, roads, accommodation work area, people and material movers.

A5 | GENERAL PLANNING

A5

B | EXCAVATIONS AND FOUNDATIONS

C | PRIMARY STRUCTURE

D | BUILDING ELEMENTS AND BUILDING SERVICES

E | CIVIL ENGINEERING

## Specific hazard identification

**Possible considerations:**

- **Sequence** – What is the proposed sequence of construction?
- **Layout** – Ensure site layout proposals reflect the construction sequence. Has it been reviewed since last process change?
- **Phased access** – Is there adequate access onto site throughout all phases of the work?
- **Interfaces** – Where have access routes for plant and personnel been defined for each phase? Separation?
- **Services protection** – Define routes and protection for temporary and permanent site services.
- **Site storage** – Where is there adequate allowance for site storage?
- **Welfare** – Where is there space for welfare facilities and site offices?
- **Cranage** – What are the proposals for location of cranes?
- **Security** – What is site work area security during work activities for operatives?
- **Any others?**

## Prompts

- Plant and machinery
- Vehicle/Pedestrians
- Sequence of construction
- Storage
- Welfare accommodation
- Access – temporary/permanent
  – vertical/horizontal
- Services (temp/permanent)
- Cranage (vertical movement)
- Conveyance (horizontal movement)
- Site access roads
- Temporary works
- Control measures
- Emergency services
- Fire prevention
- Fire-fighting
- Adjacent occupiers

## Hazards consideration in design

| Stage | Considerations and issues | Possible design options to avoid or mitigate hazards identified for site layout |
|---|---|---|
| Concept design | • Why this layout?<br>• Vehicle/Pedestrian Separation<br>• Site ergonomics<br>• Block location<br>• Project phasing<br>• Emergency provision<br>• Major movements<br>• Facilities locations<br>• System layout | • Is the site and/or its layout conducive for:<br>  – mechanical or manual construction?<br>  – off-site fabrication rather than insitu?<br>  – off site storage preferred to on-site?<br>• Ensure the site layout can accommodate labour and plant necessary to complete the work on time.<br>• Site access roads – one-way roads safer.<br>• Prepare site layouts to reduce construction activities on site and therefore reduce risks. |
| Scheme design | • System phasing<br>• Welfare facilities<br>• Deliveries/access<br>• Storage layout<br>• Handling methods<br>• Major services<br>• Element layout | • Design of phased completion to allow continued safe construction and occupation of finished work, if required.<br>• Consider width, height, load constraints for access to the work face.<br>• Having decided on site layout for construction access, ensure maintenance access is also adequate. |
| Detail design | • Working space<br>• Trade separation<br>• Routing services<br>• Positioning element<br>• Identify services<br>• Surveying | • Design to allow use of permanent roads as site roads.<br>• Ensure minimum number of handling activities created by the design.<br>• Avoid design sequence causing different trades to have to work together.<br>• Design service routes to avoid active construction. |

GENERAL PLANNING · A5

## Examples of risk mitigation (methods of solution)

| ISSUE<br>ACTION | Site layout logic | Traffic movement |
|---|---|---|
| **Avoidance**<br>Design to avoid identified hazards but beware of introducing others | Plan site strategy/ergonomics. Phasing of site layouts with phased completion. | Road layout. Location on site. |
| **Reduction**<br>Design to reduce identified hazards but beware of increasing others | Sequence each construction discipline. | Transportation study. Site road layout to be considered. |
| **Control**<br>Design to provide acceptable safeguards for all remaining identified hazards | Consider site disciplines necessary. Identify site hazards created. | Site traffic procedures. |

EXCAVATIONS AND FOUNDATIONS — B

PRIMARY STRUCTURE — C

BUILDING ELEMENTS AND BUILDING SERVICES — D

CIVIL ENGINEERING — E

## Examples of risk mitigation (issues addressed at different stages)

A terraced building in a city street is to be demolished and rebuilt. There are extensive parking restrictions in the area and the contractor will not be able to off-load materials or plant outside the site perimeter. There is no space available for unloading between the site perimeter and the proposed building.

| Concept design | Scheme design | Detail design |
|---|---|---|
| Temporary vehicle access will be designed into the new building as part of temporary works to reduce hazards. | The design will improve access by omitting part of the first floor during construction, allowing off-street delivery and unloading. | Omit two bays of structure at first floor level, with ground floor structure able to carry site vehicles as temporary access area. |

A 1960s office block is to be extensively refurbished. The existing heating systems are to be replaced with full air-conditioning and the concrete cladding units are to be replaced with insulated aluminium and glass cladding. The office must be kept operational as far as possible, consistent with the extensive refurbishment.

| Concept design | Scheme design | Detail design |
|---|---|---|
| Options reviewed indicate hazard reduction with a full structural scaffold to carry out building refurbishment works, despite the restriction the scaffold imposes on site layout. | The facade scaffold layout will be designed to be amended to follow the refurbishment programme of activities and provide temporary support for the replacement of cladding units. | Design of structural scaffold to span access into the building loading bays for delivery vehicles to avoid unloading in the site area. |

A
5

GENERAL PLANNING

B

EXCAVATIONS
AND FOUNDATIONS

C

PRIMARY STRUCTURE

D

BUILDING ELEMENTS
AND BUILDING SERVICES

E

CIVIL ENGINEERING

## Related issues

References within this document

| References | Related issues |
|---|---|
| A1 | Surrounding environment could influence decisions on site layout. |
| A2 | Site clearance will facilitate site layout planning. |
| A4 | Access onto the site will be an integral part of the plan for the site layout. |
| B1-B3 | Excavation will cause sequential implementation of site layout. |
| B4-7 | Foundations as an early activity will determine site layout. |
| C1-C4 | The supply of concrete and the installation of concrete structures will determine site layout. |
| C5-C6 | Structural steel members, if significant in size and quantity will affect site layout. |
| D1 | External cladding delivery and installation will interact with site layout. |
| E2 | Roads integral/adjacent to the site will have a determining effect on site layout. |
| E3 | Railways and their safety requirements are likely to affect site layout. |

## References for further guidance

Primary general references and background information given in Section 4

### Primary

- HSE G47 Avoiding danger from underground services
- HSE INDG258 Safe work in confined spaces
- HSE HSG141 Electrical safety on construction sites
- HSE GS6 Avoidance of danger from overhead electric power lines

### Secondary

- Building Employers Confederation (1995) Fire prevention on construction sites; Joint Code of Practice
- HSE HSG66 Protection of workers and the general public during development on contaminated land
- HSE INDG148 Reversing Vehicles
- CIRIA SP78 (1991) Building on derelict land
- CIRIA SP57 (1988) Handling of materials on site
- CIRIA PR70 (1999) Guide to assessing and managing noise on construction sites
- DoT, Interdepartmental committee on the redevelopment of contaminated Land (ICRCL)
- Guidance note 17/78 Notes on the development and after-use of land-fill sites 1990

### Background

- CIRIA SP38 (1985) Simple noise screens for site use
- Doran, D (2004) Site engineers manual (Whittles)

### Classification

**CAWS** Group A, **CEWS** Class A, **CI/SfB** Code (--)(A5)

# Group B – Excavations and foundations
## 1 – General excavation

Read the Introduction before using the following guidelines

## Scope

**Excavations for:**

- Foundations – buildings structures (bridges, retaining walls).
- Trenches – services, drainage, walls.
- Earthwork cuttings – road works, railways, services, water courses, minerals.
- Basements/shafts – buildings, drainage, services.
- Pits – ponds, waste disposal, archaeology.
- Heritage sites.

## Exclusions

- Cofferdams and caissons – work adjacent to deep water, working in compressed air (see E7).
- Tunnels.
- Unexploded bombs.

## Major hazards

Refer to the Introduction for details of accident types and health risks

**Buried/crushed/trapped**
Collapse of insufficiently supported sides of excavation. Undermining adjacent structures.

**Falls**
People, objects, supports, plant/machinery, materials. Unauthorised access.

**Plant and machinery**
Crushed/trapped/hit by plant falling/running into excavation. Fumes (eg carbon monoxide).

**Intrusive occurrences**
Groundwater, sewage, flooding. Fire, explosion, smoke, gas leakage, methane

**Health hazards**
Contaminated ground/water.
Toxic chemicals.
Asbestos.
Microbiological diseases.
Dust and allergens.
Skin irritants.

**Services**
Electrocution.
Gas pipelines.
Sewage and process effluents.

**GENERAL PLANNING** — A

**EXCAVATIONS AND FOUNDATIONS** — B / I

**PRIMARY STRUCTURE** — C

**BUILDING ELEMENTS AND BUILDING SERVICES** — D

**CIVIL ENGINEERING** — E

# B1 Group B – Excavations and foundations
## 1 – General excavation

A — GENERAL PLANNING

B1 — EXCAVATIONS AND FOUNDATIONS

C — PRIMARY STRUCTURE

D — BUILDING ELEMENTS AND BUILDING SERVICES

E — CIVIL ENGINEERING

## Specific hazard identification

**Possible key considerations:**

- **Site survey** - What are site conditions?
- **Ground Investigation** - Water table and slope stability?
- **Surface water** - What is local topography? Where are rivers, lakes, canals, ponds, etc.?
- **Working space** - What plant is required for backfilling?
- **Stockpile/disposal** - What are length and location of temporary roads and traffic routes to tip?
- **Adjacent property** - What are the position, type and use?
- **Services** - Where are they located?
- **Any others?**

## Prompts

- Historical records
- Archaeology
- Contaminated land
- Waterborne diseases
- Access/egress
- Existing outfalls and vents
- Environment: general public, weather, buildings
- Working procedures

## Hazards consideration in design

| Stage | Considerations and issues | Possible design options to avoid or mitigate hazards identified for general excavation |
|---|---|---|
| Concept design | • Why excavate? <br> • Structure location and layout <br> • Site history <br> • Materials <br> • Ground investigation <br> • Adjacent structure details <br> • Watercourses <br> • Disposal of excavated materials <br> • Services <br> • Slope stability <br> • Working space <br> • Waste disposal/haul routes <br> • Stabilise excavation <br> • Drainage | • An investigation of local earthworks could identify suitable minimum excavation site slopes. <br> • Design to avoid possibility of excavation undermining adjacent buildings. <br> • Consider possible locations of hard routes and tip sites to have least effect on construction and local community. <br> • Ensure that ground investigation will detect likely site-specific contamination. <br> • The ground investigation should relate to a range of option designs for the proposed structure. |
| Scheme design | | • In low-lying waterlogged ground, consider dewatering methods to stabilise excavations. <br> • For sites with limited working space, consider excavation within piled supports. <br> • Assess risk of diverting services versus alternative of working around them. |
| Detail design | | • For bored pile side supports in contaminated ground, consider handling and disposal of spoil. <br> • Consider shoring options for adjacent structure, to maximise working space within site excavation. <br> • Consider surface water drainage system to mitigate flooding of excavation. |

## Examples of risk mitigation (methods of solution)

| ISSUE<br><br>ACTION | Flooding | Unstable ground |
|---|---|---|
| **Avoidance**<br>Design to avoid identified hazards but beware of introducing others | Raise level of building. | Stabilise ground. |
| **Reduction**<br>Design to reduce identified hazards but beware of increasing others | Change foundation design from pads to piles. | Minimise depth of excavation. Batter side slopes. |
| **Control**<br>Design to provide acceptable safeguards for all remaining identified hazards | Consider grout curtain, well-pointing or other drainage. | Outline appropriate propping requirements. |

Sidebar labels:
- GENERAL PLANNING — A
- EXCAVATIONS AND FOUNDATIONS — B 1
- PRIMARY STRUCTURE — C
- BUILDING ELEMENTS AND BUILDING SERVICES — D
- CIVIL ENGINEERING — E

## Examples of risk mitigation (issues addressed at different stages)

Buildings are to be demolished within an urban environment to provide a new shopping arcade with basement car parking. Neighbouring buildings abut the development site. There must be agreed and acceptable methods of work to prevent the collapse of excavations and buildings.

| Concept design | Scheme design | Detail design |
|---|---|---|
| Identify history of site. Provide fully engineered retaining wall(s). | Consider new/existing structure interface and possible demolition/excavation techniques. Stability of excavation paramount. Restrict horizontal wall movements. | Retaining walls left in place for the underground car park. Consider additional methods of wall stabilisation, permanent or temporary. Consider access needs for construction and of local populace during the works. |

A proposed leisure centre is to be constructed on stable made-up ground. The proposed excavation for foundations and services could be in contaminated ground.

| Concept design | Scheme design | Detail design |
|---|---|---|
| Obtain historical records/surveys of site, detailing extent of contamination, from client. Avoid excavation in areas of known toxicity. Locate services in areas where there is no contamination, if possible. | Avoid contact with contaminants. Reduce contact by design of capping layer or use of driven piles to minimise ground disturbance. Test for types of waste product. | Consider implications for unavoidable works in contaminated area and provide relevant information to the Planning Supervisor. Put services in ducts to minimise future ground disturbance. |

# Group B – Excavations and foundations
## 1 – General excavation

A — GENERAL PLANNING

B1 — EXCAVATIONS AND FOUNDATIONS

C — PRIMARY STRUCTURE

D — BUILDING ELEMENTS AND BUILDING SERVICES

E — CIVIL ENGINEERING

## Related issues

References within this document

| References | Related issues |
|---|---|
| A1 | Local environment should be protected from the hazards associated with excavations. OH + UG services may need diversion, temporary support or protection. Adjacent structures (including walls) may need temporary support, additional support (shoring), underpinning, etc. |
| A2 | Demolition could precede excavation. Locate the health and safety file. |
| A3 | Ground investigations should include testing for toxic materials, soil density, gasses, stability and groundwater details. |
| A4 | Access/egress routes should be suitable for emergency services and for assumed construction plant. |
| A5 | Site layout should be related to the working space available, the excavation plant to be used and the size of the site. |
| B2 | - deep basements and shafts |
| B3 | - trenches for foundations and services |
| B4 | - retaining walls |
| E1 | Working space availability on a small site accentuates the hazards of excavation. Careful planning is required. |
| E2,E3 | Excavation adjacent to roads and railways should include for safe clearance distances. |
| E6,E7 | Working near water introduces a greater risk that the excavation may flood. |
|  | For issues associated with specific excavation work, refer to other sections in this group, eg: |

## References for further guidance

Primary general references and background information given in Section 4

### Primary

- CIRIA R97 (1992) Trenching practice
- CIRIA R130 (1993) Methane: its occurrence and hazards in construction
- HSE HSG47 Avoiding danger from underground services
- HSE HSG66 Protection of workers and the general public during the development of contaminated land
- HSE CIS8 (revised) Safety in excavations
- HSE INDG258 Safe work in confined spaces
- Trenter, N A (2001) Earthworks: a guide (Thomas Telford)
- CPA (2006) Safety in Shoring – the Shoring Equipment Manual of the Construction Plant-hire Association

### Secondary

- HSE GS6 Avoidance of danger from overhead electric power lines
- HSE GS29 Parts 1 to 4 Health and safety in demolition work
- CIRIA C515 (2000) Groundwater control – design and practice
- CIRIA SP32 (1984) Construction over abandoned mineworkings
- CIRIA PR77 (2000) Prop loads in large braced excavations
- CIRIA C591 (2003) Infrastructure cuttings: condition appraisal and remedial treatment
- CIRIA C592 (2003) Infrastructure embankments: condition appraisal and remedial treatment

### Background

- BS 6031:1981 Code of practice for earthworks
- BS 8002:1994 Earth retaining structures

### Classification

**CAWS** Group D,     **CEWS** Class E,     **CI/SfB** Code (1-)C

Read the Introduction before using the following guidelines

## Scope

- Basements for buildings, multi-storey offices, residential block, warehouses, car parks, etc.
- Large diameter access shafts (diameters greater than 3 metres).

## Exclusions

- Piles up to 3 metres diameter (see B6).
- Shafts for mining industry.
- Cofferdams (see E7)

## Major hazards

Refer to the Introduction for details of accident types and health risks

**Falls**
Falling into excavation or shaft. Debris or materials dropped into shaft or excavation.

**Buried/crushed/trapped**
Excavation collapse due to lack of or insufficient support.

**Health hazards**
Contaminated ground and water.

**Services**
Gas pipelines.
Electrocution.
Flooding by water or effluent.

**Ground effects**
Sudden inrush or ground water.
Mudslides.
Artesian boiling.
Methane.

**Plant and machinery**
Crushed/trapped/hit by plant in excavation.
Liquid fuels and exhaust fumes.

GENERAL PLANNING — A

EXCAVATIONS AND FOUNDATIONS — B2

PRIMARY STRUCTURE — C

BUILDING ELEMENTS AND BUILDING SERVICES — D

CIVIL ENGINEERING — E

**A** — GENERAL PLANNING

**B2** — EXCAVATIONS AND FOUNDATIONS

**C** — PRIMARY STRUCTURE

**D** — BUILDING ELEMENTS AND BUILDING SERVICES

**E** — CIVIL ENGINEERING

## Specific hazard identification

**Possible key considerations:**

- **Site survey** - Where are adjacent structures and services located?
- **Ground investigation** - What condition is soil, what is water table level?
- **Hydrology** - Where are water courses and aquifers?
- **Gases** - What level of ventilation is required?
- **Working space** - What is required for working ramps, stockpiling, deliveries of machinery?
- **Supports** - What systems will be appropriate?
- **Technological developments** - How can these be incorporated?
- **Any others?**

## Prompts

- Historical records
- Archaeology
- Contaminated land
- Waterborne diseases
- Access/egress
- Existing outfalls and vents
- Environment: general public, weather, buildings
- Working procedures

## Hazards consideration in design

| Stage | Considerations and issues | Possible design options to avoid or mitigate hazards identified for deep basements and shafts |
|---|---|---|
| Concept design | • Why excavate?<br>• Structure location and layout<br>• Site history<br>• Materials<br>• Ground investigation<br>• Adjacent structure details<br>• Watercourses<br>• Disposal of excavated materials<br>• Services<br>• Slope stability<br>• Working space<br>• Waste disposal/haul routes<br>• Stabilise excavation<br>• Drainage | • On the basis of site investigation, determine excavation methods to be excluded and identify hazardous materials and ground water problems to be addressed.<br>• Consider excavation proposals to minimise the effects on overhead and underground services or divert services either temporarily or permanently.<br>• Consider excavation within contiguous bored piles which will form permanent walls (eg for a basement).<br>• Ensure ground investigation confirms the extent and type of any contamination. |
| Scheme design | | • Ensure ground investigation confirms the extent and type of any contamination.<br>• Excavation must not compromise the structural integrity of adjacent buildings. (Consider effects on ground stability.)<br>• Design to take into account working space available and effects on local environment. |
| Detail design | | • Support details should be sufficient to contain or exclude contaminants.<br>• For excluded material, consider safe methods of disposal.<br>• Appropriate sharing techniques of adjacent buildings need to be identified (eg ground anchors).<br>• Design to identify appropriate practical and safe temporary access.<br>• Designer's assumptions on construction, sequence and methods to be identified in health and safety plan.<br>• Organise advance diversion of services by the service provider. |

## Group B – Excavations and foundations
## 2 – Deep basements and shafts

### Examples of risk mitigation (methods of solution)

| ACTION ⟍ ISSUE | Collapse | Methane from the ground |
|---|---|---|
| **Avoidance**<br>Design to avoid identified hazards but beware of introducing others | Design for shaft construction and inspection using remote control methods (eg robotics). | Incorporation of a gas – impermeable membrane is the first construction activity. |
| **Reduction**<br>Design to reduce identified hazards but beware of increasing others | Assume mechanical excavation only, with operator in safety cab at all times. | Install continuous mechanical ventilation. |
| **Control**<br>Design to provide acceptable safeguards for all remaining identified hazards | Manual operations to be easy and of short duration, within the protected area. | Ventilation system activated by gas sensor |

### Examples of risk mitigation (issues addressed at different stages)

Part of a railway terminus is to be sold for property development.
The site contains an abandoned shaft and connecting tunnels which must be isolated from tunnels still in use.

| Concept design | Scheme design | Detail design |
|---|---|---|
| Consider condition of shaft and possible re-use, as alternatives to backfilling. | Does isolation require local breakage and removal of the tunnel linings, or will substantial "plugs" be sufficient? | Check that there is a sequence of filling which keeps escape routes open and minimises depth of uncured/fluid backfill material. |

A bridge construction requires the sinking of vertical shafts to complete the pier foundations. Ground investigation has revealed the presence of hard granite boulders which precludes boring techniques.

| Concept design | Scheme design | Detail design |
|---|---|---|
| Consider possible and appropriate mechanical and/or manual excavation techniques. | Consider appropriate excavation techniques, related to location, access, topography, ground stability, plant. | Materials disposal, temporary access, stockpile. Protection of personnel in hole - support design. |

**A** GENERAL PLANNING

**B2** EXCAVATIONS AND FOUNDATIONS

**C** PRIMARY STRUCTURE

**D** BUILDING ELEMENTS AND BUILDING SERVICES

**E** CIVIL ENGINEERING

## Related issues

References within this document

| References | Related issues |
|---|---|
| A1 | Local environment should be protected from the hazards associated with excavations. In particular, adjacent structures (including walls) may need temporary support, additional support (shoring), underpinning, etc. Consider also movements of local populace and location of services/utilities. |
| A3 | Ground investigations should include testing for toxic materials from former use, soil density, gases, stability and ground water details. |
| A4 | Access/egress routes should be kept clean, clear of obstructions and be suitable for emergency services. |
| A5 | Site layout should be related to the working space available, the excavation plant to be used and the size of the site. |
| E1 | Working space on small sites accentuate the hazards of excavation. |
| E2,E3 | Excavation adjacent to roads and railways should include safe clearance distances and/or controls for site personnel together with control of excavation traffic. |
| E6,E7 | Working near water introduces a greater risk that the excavation may flood. |

## References for further guidance

Primary general references and background information given in Section 4

### Primary

- HSE HSG47 Avoiding danger from underground services
- HSE HSG66 Protection of workers and the general public during the development of contaminated land
- HSE INDG258 Safe work in confined spaces
- HSE GS6 Avoidance of danger from overhead electric power lines
- HSE CIS8 (revised) Safety in excavations
- BS 8008:1996 Guide to safety precautions and procedures for the construction and descent of machine-bored shafts for piling and other purposes

### Secondary

- CIRIA R139 (1995) Water resisting basements
- CIRIA C517 (1999) Temporary propping of deep excavations: guidance on design

### Background

- Institution of Structural Engineers (2004) Design and construction of deep basements including cut-and-cover structures
- Puller M, (2003) Deep Excavations: a practical manual. 2nd ed (Thomas Telford)
- Tomlinson M J, Foundation design and construction (Prentice-Hall)
- BS 8004:1986 Code of practice for foundations
- CIRIA C580 (2003) Embedded retaining walls – guidance for economic design

### Classification

**CAWS** Group G, **CI/SfB** Code (1-)C

Read the Introduction before using the following guidelines

## Scope

- Trenches for strip foundations and pad foundations.
- Trenches for public utilities, services, pipe lines, drains, etc.
- Pits and pipe jacking.

## Exclusions

- Deep pier foundations, underpinning.
- Trench depths > 6m and below water.
- Trenches adjacent to deep water.

## Major hazards

Refer to the Introduction for details of accident types and health risks

**Services**
Electrocution.
Gas pipelines.
Sewage and process effluents.

**Health hazards**
Water-borne toxins and diseases.
Methane.
Asbestos.

**Inundation**
Flooding, drowning.
Chemical waste, effluents.

**Plant and machinery**
Vehicles too close cause trench side to collapse.
Fuel vapours and exhaust fumes.
Pneumatic tools (vibration white finger).

**Falls**
No guard rails, congested sites, lack of working space.

**Buried/crushed/trapped**
Materials/spoil, falls into trench. Trench collapse due to insufficient support.

A — GENERAL PLANNING

B3 — EXCAVATIONS AND FOUNDATIONS

C — PRIMARY STRUCTURE

D — BUILDING ELEMENTS AND BUILDING SERVICES

E — CIVIL ENGINEERING

## Specific hazard identification

**Possible key considerations:**

- **Site survey** - Where are the services?
- **Services** - Do services need support across trench?
- **General investigation** - What are soil types? What is the water table level? Could the trench flood?
- **Hydrology** - Where are the water courses? Will surface water run-off be a problem?
- **Side supports** - What systems are appropriate for the known ground conditions?
- **Gases** - What assessment is required to decide ventilation?
- **Working space** - What space is required for deliveries, stockpiling, ramps, haul road? Ensure safe distance from trench.
- **Backfilling** - What compaction can be carried out without using hand-held machines?
- **Any others?**

## Prompts

- Historical records
- Archaeology (where appropriate)
- Contaminated land
- Protection of public
- Access/egress
- Illumination
- Waste disposal
- Noise/vibration
- Emergency procedures
- Propriety systems
- Confined space working
- Pipe jacking
- Trenchless methods

## Hazards consideration in design

| Stage | Considerations and issues | Possible design options to avoid or mitigate hazards identified for trenches for foundations and services |
|---|---|---|
| Concept design | • Why trenches?<br>• Site inspection<br>• Site history<br>• Access/egress<br>• Working space | • Establish details of foundations of existing structures and previous work at the site.<br>• Identify necessary working space in relation to existing buildings and services.<br>• Identify (and reduce) effects on local environment and services.<br>• Look for alternative routes to avoid deep trenches and steeply sloping ground.<br>• Establish ground conditions |
| Scheme design | • Environment<br>• Topography<br>• Services<br>• Ground conditions<br>• Contamination<br>• Rights of way<br>• Plant/machinery | • Identify safe working space for excavation depths required.<br>• The presence of water can create instability. Minimise need and depth of excavation.<br>• Consider construction techniques to avoid need for trench excavation (eg local excavation and pipe jacking or slit trench and automatic cable laying). |
| Detail design | • Trench supports<br>• Drainage proposals<br>• Adjacent structures<br>• Working procedures | • To minimise effects of water, include for drainage system to restrict/divert ground waste and run-off.<br>• Consider problems of existing services which cross proposed excavation. Identify necessary support systems.<br>• Minimise the time and complexity of manual operations (eg jointing) to be carried out in trench. |

# Group B – Excavations and foundations
## 3 – Trenches for foundations and services

## Examples of risk mitigation (methods of solution)

| ISSUE / ACTION | Collapse of adjacent foundations | Flooding from adjacent watercourse |
|---|---|---|
| **Avoidance** Design to avoid identified hazards but beware of introducing others | Relocate or use shallower trench or use trenchless construction. | Relocate trench. Do not excavate near watercourse. |
| **Reduction** Design to reduce identified hazards but beware of increasing others | Install underpinning or temporary works ahead of trenching. | Redirect watercourse, reinforce banks, extend flood defences. |
| **Control** Design to provide acceptable safeguards for all remaining identified hazards | Monitor movement and specify that appropriate plant and materials always to be available. | Allow for the early construction of an appropriate system of drains and pumps. |

## Examples of risk mitigation (issues addressed at different stages)

A communications company wants to provide the option of cable TV to all properties in a township of historical interest.

| Concept design | Scheme design | Detail design |
|---|---|---|
| Can the existing telephone cable network be used? Is there major work planned by other communication/utility companies? | Consider trench sharing with other services. Keep away from existing services and use combined dig-and-lay techniques. | Programme the works to avoid bad weather, local events, and tourist seasons. |

A two-storey townhouse is to be constructed in an urban setting. Properties are located on each side and to the rear. The site has a road frontage. Excavation for strip footing foundations is in topsoil/clay.

| Concept design | Scheme design | Detail design |
|---|---|---|
| Layout to consider ground slope, services location, access. Consider also adjacent buildings/structures. | Consider stepped footings on sloping ground. Services, water table, stockpile of excavated material. | Stepped footings reduce excavated depth. Drainage measures to reduce flooding risk. Plant location during concreting. Use concrete backfill to reduce settlement. |

**A** GENERAL PLANNING

**B 3** EXCAVATIONS AND FOUNDATIONS

**C** PRIMARY STRUCTURE

**D** BUILDING ELEMENTS AND BUILDING SERVICES

**E** CIVIL ENGINEERING

## Related issues

References within this document

| References | Related issues |
|---|---|
| A1 | Local environment should be protected from the hazards associated with excavations. Identify also location of services/building utilities. |
| A3 | Ground investigations should include testing for toxic materials, soil density, gases, stability and ground water details. |
| A4 | Access/egress routes should be kept clean, clear of obstructions and be suitable for emergency services. |
| A5 | Site layout should be related to the working space available, designer's assumptions of excavation plant to be used and the size of the site. |
| E1 | Working space on small sites accentuates the hazards of excavation. Consider practicalities of excavation and construction sequence. |
| E2,E3 | Excavation adjacent to roads and railways should include safe clearance distances and/or suitable protection for site personnel. |
| E6,E7 | Working near water introduces a greater risk that the excavation may flood. |

## References for further guidance

Primary general references and background information given in Section 4

### Primary

- CIRIA R97 (1993) Trenching practice. Second edition
- CIRIA SP147 (1998) Trenchless and minimum excavation techniques: planning and selection
- HSE CIS8 (revised) Safety in excavations
- DTLR (2001) Safety at street works and road works: a code of practice (TSO)
- Trenter, N A (2001) Earthworks: a guide (Thomas Telford)
- CPA (2006) Safety in Shoring – the Shoring Equipment Manual of the Construction Plant-hire Association

### Secondary

- HSE HSG47 Avoiding danger from underground services
- HSE HSG66 Protection of workers and the general public during the development of contaminated land
- HSE INDG258 Safe work in confined spaces
- HSE GS6 Avoidance of danger from overhead electric power lines

### Background

- CIRIA R130 (1993) Methane: its occurrence and hazards in construction
- CIRIA TN112 (1983) Pipe jacking: a state-of-the-art review (microfiche)
- Curtin, W G et al (2006) Structural foundation designers' manual (Blackwell)

### Classification

**CAWS** Group D,P&R **CEWS** Classes E,I,J,K,L&Z **CI/SfB** Code (1-)C

Read the Introduction before using the following guidelines

## Scope

- Single-storey basements, drainage chambers, service ducts.
- Earthworks/cuttings: roadworks, railways, watercourses, landscaping.
- Temporary retaining walls, eg sheet piles.

## Exclusions

- Deep basements and shafts (see B2).
- Cofferdams and caissons (see E7).
- Mining and work adjacent to deep water.
- Gabions.

**A** GENERAL PLANNING

**B 4** EXCAVATIONS AND FOUNDATIONS

**C** PRIMARY STRUCTURE

**D** BUILDING ELEMENTS AND BUILDING SERVICES

**E** CIVIL ENGINEERING

## Major hazards

Refer to the Introduction for details of accident types and health risks

**Buried/crushed/trapped**
Collapse of unretained material.
Collapse of incomplete and temporarily unstable wall.
Inadequate working space behind wall.

**Falls**
Into base excavation from top of incomplete wall.
Into water-filled excavation or temporarily-retained water.

**Plant and transport**
Site traffic. Slewing of concrete skip, shutters, etc.
Work adjacent to road/railway.

**Services**
Electrocution.
Gas pipelines.
Sewage and process effluents.
Emergency. communications.

**Ground movements**
Subsidence of adjacent structures.
Fractured services and waste pipes.

**Health hazards**
Noise/vibration.
Dust inhalation.
Fumes.
Water-borne diseases.
Manual handling.

**A** GENERAL PLANNING

**B4** EXCAVATIONS AND FOUNDATIONS

**C** PRIMARY STRUCTURE

**D** BUILDING ELEMENTS AND BUILDING SERVICES

**E** CIVIL ENGINEERING

## Specific hazard identification

**Possible key considerations:**

- **Site survey** - Where are service? What structures are adjacent to site? What is topography?
- **Ground investigation** - Is there evidence of earth movement? Where is water table?
- **Environment** - What are implications of site location? (eg urban, rural, next to river, railway, road).
- **Retaining wall** - What is wall to be used for? What type is it to be (eg gravity, reinforced concrete, temporary)?
- **Plant & Machinery** - What is sufficient working space for the proposed construction methods?
- **Sequences** - What are the construction sequences?
- **Access** - What access is required to rear of wall?
- **Any others?**

## Prompts

- Soil types
- Services
- Adjacent structures (foundations)
- Retaining wall type
- Plant/machinery
- Access/working space
- Weather
- Backfilling

## Hazards consideration in design

| Stage | Considerations and issues | Possible design options to avoid or mitigate hazards identified for retaining walls |
|---|---|---|
| Concept design | • Why retaining wall?<br>• Location<br>• Environment<br>• Topography<br>• Access<br>• Services | • Position could determine wall type that can be practically and safely constructed: examine options available.<br>• Consider type of wall to minimise hazard of interaction with services, particularly gas and electricity.<br>• Evaluate possible effects on adjacent structures during operation. |
| Scheme design | • Wall position<br>• Protection of property<br>• Adjacent structures<br>• Working space<br>• Temporary roads<br>• Ground investigation<br>• Retaining wall types<br>• Plant/machinery<br>• Backfilling<br>• Drainage | • Design to minimise depth of excavations (eg incorporate a piled base or grout curtain).<br>• Consider excavation techniques in relation to ground conditions, working space and environmental constraints. (Relate to wall design.)<br>• Identify necessary ground and surface water control systems.<br>• Eliminate need for operatives to access rear of wall in confined spaces.<br>• Backfilling prohibited or limited until a certain stage of wall construction. |
| Detail design | • Ground stability<br>• Maintenance<br>• Advance works<br>• Temporary live loads during construction | • Consider temporary diversion of services during retaining wall construction.<br>• Wall design to include facilities for ease of maintenance.<br>• Prefabricated units to provide fixing locations for permanent or temporary guard rails. |

## Examples of risk mitigation (methods of solution)

| ACTION / ISSUE | Ground slippage | Gas pipes crossing line of wall |
|---|---|---|
| **Avoidance** — Design to avoid identified hazards but beware of introducing others | Pre-stabilise ground. | Change route of wall to avoid gas pipes. |
| **Reduction** — Design to reduce identified hazards but beware of increasing others | Consider piles, soil nailing, ground anchors. | Change design of wall in vicinity of gas pipes (eg change ground levels or select shallower and wider base). |
| **Control** — Design to provide acceptable safeguards for all remaining identified hazards | Outline possible staged construction sequence. | Specify robust protection to be incorporated into the permanent works. |

## Examples of risk mitigation (issues addressed at different stages)

An existing busy urban road is to be widened. Land is not available either side. The widening is therefore to be completed on line. The existing cutting slope will require a retaining wall (height 5 metres).

| Concept design | Scheme design | Detail design |
|---|---|---|
| Consider environmentally appropriate solutions and proposals for existing road traffic. Site history - slope stability. | Bored piles reduce excavation hazard and noise and effects on existing traffic; locate services. | Access/egress site details. Allow for temporary diversion of traffic/ lane closures. |

A building is to be constructed within an urban environment. Car parking is to be made available in the basement. The surrounding properties are shops, offices, residential blocks.

| Concept design | Scheme design | Detail design |
|---|---|---|
| Consider proximity of adjacent properties and road traffic. Relate to environment and location. Noise and vibration issues. | Consider constructing a retaining wall prior to basement excavation. Ground investigation (water-bearing strata). Consider diaphragm wall, combined with ground anchors. | Precast panels/in-situ concrete (underpin adjacent building). |

GENERAL PLANNING — A

EXCAVATIONS AND FOUNDATIONS — B 4

PRIMARY STRUCTURE — C

BUILDING ELEMENTS AND BUILDING SERVICES — D

CIVIL ENGINEERING — E

A — GENERAL PLANNING

B4 — EXCAVATIONS AND FOUNDATIONS

C — PRIMARY STRUCTURE

D — BUILDING ELEMENTS AND BUILDING SERVICES

E — CIVIL ENGINEERING

## Related issues

References within this document

| References | Related issues |
|---|---|
| A1 | Local environment should be protected from the hazards associated with excavations. |
| A3 | Ground investigation should include tests for toxic materials, soil density, gases, stability and groundwater details. |
| A4 | Access/egress routes should be kept clean, clear of obstructions and be suitable for emergency services. |
| A5 | Site layout should be related to the working space available, the excavation plant to be used and the size of the site. |
| E1 | Working space on small sites accentuates the hazards of excavation. |
| E2,E3 | Excavation adjacent to roads and railways should include safe clearance distances and/or suitable protection for site personnel. |
| E6,E7 | Working near water introduces a greater risk that the excavation may flood. |
| B5 | Ground stabilisation may provide a safer solution. |
| | Underground/overhead services need to be carefully considered. |

## References for further guidance

Primary general references and background information given in Section 4

### Primary

- HSE INDG258 Safe work in confined spaces
- HSE GS6 Avoidance of danger from overhead power lines
- HSE GS29 Parts 1 to 4 Health and safety in demolition work
- HSE CIS8 (revised) Safety in excavations
- DTLR (2001) Safety at street works and road works: a code of practice
- CIRIA C580 (2003) Embedded retaining walls – guidance for economic design

### Secondary

- HSE HSG47 Avoiding danger from underground services
- HSE HSG66 Protection of workers and the general public during the development of contaminated land
- ICE (1996) Specification for piling and embedded retaining walls

### Background

- BS 8002:1994 Earth Retaining Structures
- BS 8006:1995 Code of Practice for strengthened/reinforced soils and other fills
- Clayton, C R I (1993) Earth pressure and earth retaining structures
- ICE (1993) Retaining structures (Thomas Telford)

### Classification

**CAWS**  Group E,     **CEWS**  Classes E,F&H,     **CI/SfB**  Code (16)

Read the Introduction before using the following guidelines

## Scope

- Vibroflotation (vibrocompaction, vibroreplacement).
- Dynamic compaction.
- Lime and cement stabilisation.
- Dewatering/band drains.
- Preloading.
- Jet grouting, permeation grouting (to improve bearing capacity).

## Exclusions

- Ground freezing.
- Stabilisation of rock masses (rock bolting, etc.).
- Slope stabilisation (soil nailing, retaining structures, etc.).
- Settlement reducing/elimination measures (eg compensation grouting).

## Major hazards

Refer to the Introduction for details of accident types and health risks

**Plant instability**
Inadequate working platform - consider bearing capacity, gradient, stability of fill (settlement), slope stability.

**Crushed/trapped**
Manoeuvring and slewing of heavy plant and equipment.

**Working environment**
Noise, vibration, fumes, asphyxiation (eg nitrogen), high pressure lines and hoses.

**Services**
Buried underground and overhead services including gas, electricity, water. Damage by drilling, driving, impact, vibration, settlement.

**Health hazards**
Contact with contaminated arisings/groundwater.
Dust and irritation from materials (eg cement and lime).

**Falls**
From plant and machinery tilted by uneven/soft ground.

**A** GENERAL PLANNING

**B5** EXCAVATIONS AND FOUNDATIONS

**C** PRIMARY STRUCTURE

**D** BUILDING ELEMENTS AND BUILDING SERVICES

**E** CIVIL ENGINEERING

## Specific hazard identification

**Possible key considerations:**

- **Access** - What provisions are necessary at each location?
- **Working space** - What needs to be provided?
- **Working platform** - Where and what is needed?
- **Services** - Where are they located?
- **Stability** - What considerations need to be made for nearby structures?
- **Workers/public** - What is their proximity?
- **Workers** - What is proximity of workers during operations?
- **Contamination** - Where is affected ground and water?
- **Materials** - What substances are hazardous to health?
- **Any others?**

## Prompts

- Access routes
- Plant size and weight
- Site survey rig details
- Services check
- Structural survey
- Noise/dust/lifting materials
- Site investigation

## Hazards consideration in design

| Stage | Considerations and issues | Possible design options to avoid or mitigate hazards identified for ground stabilisation |
|---|---|---|
| Concept design | • Why stabilise?<br>• Location of structure<br>• Overall programme | • Review reasons for stabilising (eg bearing capacity or settlement).<br>• Identify constraints and consider relocation of structure.<br>• Consider alternative types of structure, such as flexible foundations.<br>• Surveys/site investigation/desk study to enable options to be assessed systematically. |
| Scheme design | • Type of structure<br>• Surveys/site investigation/desk study<br>• Access<br>• Programme/sequences<br>• Interfaces<br>• Specific alternatives<br>• Depth of stabilisation | • Consider access requirements and location relative to public.<br>• Eliminate interface constraints.<br>• Consider alternative stabilisation methods? (Contact experienced specialist contractors for advice.) |
| Detail design | • Type of stabilisation material<br>• Access/haul routes<br>• Working platform | • Consider depths of treatment required by design, in relation to plant capabilities (eg can smaller plant be used?)<br>• Can an alternative stabilisation material be used (eg cement instead of lime)?<br>• Can same access points and haul roads be used throughout contract?<br>• Can working platform form part of permanent works? |

## Examples of risk mitigation (methods of solution)

| ACTION \ ISSUE | Use of surcharging | Use of lime piles |
|---|---|---|
| **Avoidance**<br>Design to avoid identified hazards but beware of introducing others | Avoid stabilisation by phased construction (eg allow periods for the ground to consolidate between defined stages of construction). | Avoid hazard of lime piles by using stone columns? |
| **Reduction**<br>Design to reduce identified hazards but beware of increasing others | Consider preloading or drainage to induce settlement. | Minimise depth of ground treatment to allow lighter/smaller plant to be used? |
| **Control**<br>Design to provide acceptable safeguards for all remaining identified hazards | Outline appropriate monitoring locations and criteria. Change the building/structure performance specification for movement. | Outline hazards of plant instability and need to design working platform. |

## Examples of risk mitigation (issues addressed at different stages)

A haul road at a supermarket site is to be constructed on a wet clay subgrade, to enable use of road lorries/tippers. To save on granular material, it is proposed to stabilise the clay subgrade using quick-lime.

| Concept design | Scheme design | Detail design |
|---|---|---|
| Consider re-aligning haul road and the use of all terrain dump trucks. | To avoid hazard of anhydrous quick-lime, consider alternative forms of stabilisation, eg<br><br>a) Geogrid reinforced, granular roadway with geotextile separation membrane.<br><br>b) Re-sequence earthmoving to summer period. | To reduce risk associated with exposure to quick-lime, specify lime graded between 3mm and 12mm (to reduce dusting). |

An embankment adjacent to an estuary is to be founded on soft clay. It is proposed that vibro-replacement with stone columns will be used to reduce settlement of the embankment.

| Concept design | Scheme design | Detail design |
|---|---|---|
| To avoid hazard of plant instability, consider re-locating embankment onto stronger ground or the use of lightweight fill to reduce loading. | To avoid hazard of heavy plant (70 tonne) operating on soft material, consider differential and total settlement criteria to see if a shallow foundation type can be adopted (eg. geocell mattress/raft). | Consider using smaller plant. Outline need to plan/sequence work carefully (eg work along embankment using stone columns to act as foundation to haul road and working platform for vibroreplacement plant). Separate public and workers from haul road (reroute footpaths) |

**A** — GENERAL PLANNING

**B 5** — EXCAVATIONS AND FOUNDATIONS

**C** — PRIMARY STRUCTURE

**D** — BUILDING ELEMENTS AND BUILDING SERVICES

**E** — CIVIL ENGINEERING

## B5 — Group B – Excavations and foundations
## 5 – Ground stabilisation

## Related issues

References within this document

| References | Related issues |
| --- | --- |
| A1 | Surrounding environment will be affected by ground stabilisation work. |
| A2 | Site clearance works may be able to accommodate access provision for future stabilisation work. |
| A3 | Site investigation will be necessary to determine the criteria for future stabilisation work. |
| A4 | Access onto the site will be necessary for the plant. |
| A5 | Site layout determines the extent of the stabilisation necessary. |
| B1 | General excavation may require the use of stabilisation measures. |
| E2 | Working near roads may be undertaken while road is in use. |
| E3 | Working near railways may be undertaken while railway is in use. |
| E6,E7 | Working near water may be a major consideration. |
| | Contamination may be caused by ground treatment processes (eg groundwater). |

## References for further guidance

Primary general references and background information given in Section 4

### Primary

- CIRIA SP123 (1996) Soil reinforcement with geotextiles
- CIRIA B11 (1991) Prefabricated vertical drains
- CIRIA R95 (1982) Health and safety aspects of ground treatment materials (microfiche)
- ICE Works Construction Guide "Ground stabilisation, deep compaction and grouting"
- CIRIA C637 (2005) Soil Nailing
- CIRIA R113 (1986) Control of groundwater for temporary works (microfiche)

### Secondary

- CIRIA C514 (2000) Grouting for ground engineering
- HSE CIS8 (revised) Safety in excavations
- HSE – Be Safe, Be Sure

### Background

- Construction Industry Training Board CITB/FPS Document GE 708 Safety on piling sites
- CIRIA SP136 (1996) Site guide to construction of foundations
- Bell, F G (1993) Engineering treatment of soils (Spon)
- Moseley, M P (2004) Ground improvement. 2nd ed (Blackie)

### Classification

**CAWS** Group D, **CEWS** Classes E&C, **CI/SfB** Code (11)

Read the Introduction before using the following guidelines

## Scope

- Foundation piles - bored, driven, timber, steel, concrete.
- Load testing of piles.
- Shafts < 3m diameter.
- Installation of sheet piles.

## Exclusions

- Piles for underpinning (see B7).
- Piling over water (see E6).
- Piling next to railways and/or roads (see E2, E3).

## Major hazards

Refer to the Introduction for details of accident types and health risks

**Plant instability**
Inadequate working platform for equipment - considerations such as: bearing capacity, gradient, stability, variability of ground conditions.

**Plant and Machinery**
Lifting, slewing and pitching of casings, piles and reinforcement cages. Movement of piling rigs, Delivery of materials.

**Working environment**
Noise, vibration, exhaust fumes, trips, open bores/excavations, impact from spoil falling off auger.

**Services**
Buried underground and overhead services including gas, electricity, water and drainage by drilling, driving, impact, vibration, settlement.

**Health hazards**
Contact with contaminated arisings/groundwater.
Dust and irritation from materials (eg bentonite and cement).

**Collapse of excavation**
Insufficient support of bores/excavation results in collapse, including loss of slimy support materials (eg drains). Collapse during inspection of pile base, or collapse due to construction delays.

GENERAL PLANNING  **A**

EXCAVATIONS AND FOUNDATIONS  **B6**

PRIMARY STRUCTURE  **C**

BUILDING ELEMENTS AND BUILDING SERVICES  **D**

CIVIL ENGINEERING  **E**

A — GENERAL PLANNING

B6 — EXCAVATIONS AND FOUNDATIONS

C — PRIMARY STRUCTURE

D — BUILDING ELEMENTS AND BUILDING SERVICES

E — CIVIL ENGINEERING

## Specific hazard identification

**Possible key considerations:**

- **Access** - What provision is required at each pile location?
- **Working space** - What needs to be provided?
- **Working platform** - Where and what is needed?
- **Services** - Where are they located?
- **Stability** - What considerations need to be made for nearby structure?
- **Workers/public** - What is the proximity?
- **Contamination** - Where is affected ground and water?
- **Materials** - What substances are hazardous to health?
- **Open pile borings** - How will these be protected?
- **Operations** - What sequences will be adopted?
- **Obstructions** - Check for underground structures and for abandoned foundations, works and services.
- **Any others?**

## Prompts

- Access routes
- Plant size
- Site survey/rig details
- Services check
- Structural survey
- Noise/dust
- Lifting materials/crane loads
- Site investigation
- Confined space/falling materials

## Hazards consideration in design

| Stage | Considerations and issues | Possible design options to avoid or mitigate hazards identified for piling |
|---|---|---|
| Concept design | • Why is piling required?<br>• Location of structure<br>• Type of structure<br>• Overall programme | • Review the reasons for piling (eg bearing capacity or settlement?).<br>• Identify constraints and consider relocation of structure.<br>• Consider alternatives (eg shallow foundations, rafts or flexible foundations such as a reinforced soil mattress).<br>• Surveys/site investigation/desk study to enable different options to be assessed systematically). |
| Scheme design | • Surveys/site investigation/desk study<br>• Access<br>• Programme/sequences<br>• Interfaces<br>• Type of pile<br>• Working platform<br>• Pile length | • Consider piling techniques to minimise noise and spreading of spoil (if ground contaminated).<br>• Identify access requirements associated with equipment (eg overhead power lines and low headroom).<br>• Programme to allow separation of site activities such as trial piling and demolition (programme and interface constraints).<br>• Consider the magnitude and distribution of structural loads in relation to constraints (eg low headroom may restrict pile size). |
| Detail design | • Obstructions<br>• Programme<br>• Temporary works | • Consider support of bore.<br>• How will obstructions such as old basements or unforeseen objects be removed if encountered?<br>• Allow sufficient programme time for method (eg Continuous Flight Auger (CFA) bored piles are quick to construct). |

# Group B – Excavations and foundations
## 6 – Piling

## Examples of risk mitigation (methods of solution)

| ACTION \ ISSUE | Piling plant on soft ground | Piling near overhead power lines |
|---|---|---|
| **Avoidance** Design to avoid identified hazards but beware of introducing others | Consider alternative foundation to avoid hazard of piling plant. | Avoid piling near power lines. |
| **Reduction** Design to reduce identified hazards but beware of increasing others | Use transfer structure to reduce number of piles, and avoid piling in the softest area. | Design alternative forms of foundations. |
| **Control** Design to provide acceptable safeguards for all remaining identified hazards | Outline allowable bearing capacity of ground. | Highlight the hazards. |

## Examples of risk mitigation (issues addressed at different stages)

An embankment is to be located beneath overhead electricity lines and adjacent to pylons. It is proposed to use bored cast in-situ concrete piles.

| Concept design | Scheme design | Detail design |
|---|---|---|
| To avoid hazard of electrocution, consider moving structure or diverting overhead power lines. If this is not possible reconsider design criteria such as differential settlement rather than total settlement. | Design developed using an increased number of smaller piles with a transfer structure. Adopt bored piles rather than driven piles to avoid hazard of pitching piles. | Use tripod rigs/cut down mast on piling rig to enable safety zone to be maintained. Detail pile reinforcement to suit headroom restrictions. |

Building layout requires high column loads to be supported. It is proposed to adopt large diameter under-reamed bored piles. Consider hazard of pile bore instability during base inspection.

| Concept design | Scheme design | Detail design |
|---|---|---|
| Consider a design that uses transfer structures to allow use of more, smaller diameter, straight shafted piles. Carry out trial pile to check underream stability? | Consider use of larger diameter shaft and smaller diameter underream. Consider reducing number of underream piles by having fewer larger diameter piles. Down rate pile base and accept inspection by CCTV. Use base grouting of pile? | Design casing to support pile shaft. Make inspection cage equal in height to uncased height. Specification of unavoidable inspection requirements to favour sampling and testing of the shortest duration possible. |

A  GENERAL PLANNING

**B 6**  EXCAVATIONS AND FOUNDATIONS

C  PRIMARY STRUCTURE

D  BUILDING ELEMENTS AND BUILDING SERVICES

E  CIVIL ENGINEERING

## Related issues

References within this document

| References | Related issues |
|---|---|
| A1 | Surrounding environment will be affected by piling operations. |
| A2 | Site clearance works should accommodate access provisions for future piling works. |
| A3 | Site investigation will be necessary to determine data for piling work. |
| A2,A3 | Ground contamination will influence choice of piling. |
| A4 | Access requirements for piling equipment is a major consideration. |
| A5 | Site layout may influence piling method. |
| B1 | General excavation requirements may influence piling methods and equipment. |
| C1,C2 | Concrete methods need to be considered. |
| E2 | Working near roads may have to be undertaken while road is in use. |
| E3 | Working near railways is usually undertaken while railway is in use. |
| E6,E7 | Working near water may be a major consideration. |
| | Underground services are a major factor in piling operations. |

## References for further guidance

Primary general references and background information given in Section 4

### Primary

- Construction Industry Training Board CITB/FPS Document GE 708 Safety on piling sites
- BS 8008:1996 A guide to safety precautions and procedures for the construction and descent of machine bored shafts for piling and other purposes
- CIRIA PG1 (1988) A review of bearing pile types
- CIRIA C703 (2003) Crane stability on site

### Secondary

- Arcelor (2005) Piling handbook. 8th ed
- CIRIA PG2–9 Piling guides (some microfiche only)
- HSE CIS8 (revised) Safety in excavations
- ICE (1996) Specification for piling and embedded retaining walls

### Background

- CIRIA SP105 (1995) Remedial treatment for contaminated land, Vol V: Excavation and disposal
- Fleming, W G K (1992) Piling engineering. 2nd ed (Blackie)
- Tomlinson, M J (2007) Pile design and construction. 5th ed (Taylor & Francis)

### Classification

**CAWS** Group D,     **CEWS** Classes O,P,N&Q,     **CI/SfB** Code (17)

Read the Introduction before using the following guidelines

## Scope

- Mass concrete underpinning.
- Pier and beam underpinning.
- Pile and beam underpinning.
- Mini-piling.

## Exclusions

- Jet grouting and permeation grouting (see B5).

## Major hazards

Refer to the Introduction for details of accident types and health risks

**Structural instability**
Inadequate stability of structure and risk to workers and occupants of the buildings.

**Crushed/trapped**
Narrow spaces and low headroom for manoeuvring heavy plant and materials. Manual handling of casings, reinforcement, trench sheets and concrete in confined spaces.

**Working environment**
Noise, vibration, fumes (confined space ventilation?).
Use of tools in confined spaces.

**Services**
Buried underground services and overhead services including gas, electricity, water inside and outside buildings. Damage by drilling, driving, impact, vibration, settlement.

**Health hazards**
Contact with contaminated arisings/groundwater, cement, concrete, adhesives, including inhalation of fumes and dusts (eg fibres from dry materials.

**Collapse of excavations**
Insufficient support results in collapse with risk of entrapment or falls and sudden water inflow/flooding.

# Group B – Excavations and foundations
## 7 – Underpinning

## Specific hazard identification

**Possible key considerations:**

- **Access** - What provisions are necessary?
- **Working space** - What needs to be provided?
- **Services** - Where are they located?
- **Stability** - What is the condition of brickwork/walls?
- **Workers/public** - What is the proximity?
- **Contamination** - Where is affected ground and water?
- **Materials** - Where are substances hazardous to health?
- **Manual handling** - What is the extent of this aspect?
- **Hand tools** - What provisions need to be made?
- **Any others?**

## Prompts

- Access routes
- Plant size
- Services
- Structural survey
- Noise/dust
- Handling materials
- Site investigation

## Hazards consideration in design

| Stage | Considerations and issues | Possible design options to avoid or mitigate hazards identified for underpinning |
|---|---|---|
| Concept design | • Why underpin?<br>• Type of structure<br>• Access | • Consider strengthening and/or repair of structure instead of underpinning.<br>• Consider removing cause of distress and repairing structure.<br>• Consider stabilising ground (eg grouting old mineworkings).<br>• Structural survey/site investigation/desk study to understand problem systematically. |
| Scheme design | • Interfaces<br>• Surveys/site investigation/desk study<br>• Type of underpinning<br>• Stability during underpinning<br>• Sequences<br>• Handling materials<br>• Work sequences | • Choice of shallow foundations may reduce hazard of entrapment.<br>• Choice of mini-piling may reduce excavation of contaminated material.<br>• Excavation may destabilise structure.<br>• Consider mini-piles and needling, which may cause less disturbance to a fragile structure. |
| Detail design | • Detailing<br>• Temporary works<br>• Monitoring | • Define sequence of support to avoid instability.<br>• Avoid starter bars.<br>• Require monitoring of structure/ground during work, having defined allowable movements. |

## Examples of risk mitigation (methods of solution)

| ISSUE<br><br>ACTION | Need to underpin | Mass concrete underpinning |
|---|---|---|
| **Avoidance**<br>Design to avoid identified hazards but beware of introducing others | Avoid underpinning by addressing cause of ground movement and repairing structure. | Avoid entrapment by avoiding descent of excavations (remote operation and inspection). |
| **Reduction**<br>Design to reduce identified hazards but beware of increasing others | Consider different types of underpinning available and hazards with each. | Reduce hazard of excavation by minimising descent. |
| **Control**<br>Design to provide acceptable safeguards for all remaining identified hazards | Outline interface issues (time, space etc). Associated with types of underpinning. | Outline need to control groundwater inflow in H&S Plan. |

A — GENERAL PLANNING

B7 — EXCAVATIONS AND FOUNDATIONS

C — PRIMARY STRUCTURE

D — BUILDING ELEMENTS AND BUILDING SERVICES

E — CIVIL ENGINEERING

## Examples of risk mitigation (issues addressed at different stages)

Structure constructed on varying depth of made ground is to be underpinned.

| Concept design | Scheme design | Detail design |
|---|---|---|
| Mass concrete underpinning chosen to avoid hazard of piling plant. Underpinning to be continuous, carried out in a "hit-and-miss" manner. | Consider dowels protruding into "miss" bays/ excavation.<br>Design for use of:<br>- bar couplers/reinforcement coupler strips, or<br>- "joggle/key" joint<br>- smaller diameter mild steel dowel bars (10/12mm diameter) that can be bent out of way. | Choose small diameter dowels. Control hazard by placing "mushroom" caps on projecting dowel bars to protect workers in trenches. |

Structure on contaminated ground is to be underpinned.

| Concept design | Scheme design | Detail design |
|---|---|---|
| The design is to consider techniques that do not involve excavation. Can the structure be strengthened or repaired without excavation? | The design will include an underpinning technique that minimises excavation and contact with contaminated material (eg mini-piles?).<br>Identify contaminants by site investigation. | Highlight need to ventilate confined spaces inside building during work. Identify need to monitor confined spaces. |

## Related issues

References within this document

| References | Related issues |
|---|---|
| A1 | Surrounding environment may be affected by the underpinning work. |
| A2 | Site clearance may be moved before work can commence. |
| A3 | Site investigation will be necessary to identify scope of work. |
| A4 | Access onto the site will be a major consideration. |
| A5 | Site layout may influence the underpinning method and temporary works. |
| B1 | General excavation may be necessary. |
| B6 | Piling may be used as a method of support. |
| C1,C2 | Concrete pumping and use will need to be considered. |
| | Groundwater level and surcharge from plant will influence stability of trench excavations. |
| | Contaminated ground will influence design and precautions. |
| E3 | Working near railways will be a major consideration in the choice of plant.. |
| E6,E7 | Working near water will involve possibility of dewatering excavation. |

## References for further guidance

Primary general references and background information given in Section 4

### Primary

- CITB Construction Site Safety Note 10 - Excavations
- HSE CIS8 (revised) Safety in excavations
- CIRIA R97 (1992) Trenching practice
- Guidelines on safe and efficient underpinning and mini-piling operations: Association of Specialist Underpinning Contractors (ASUCplus)

### Secondary

- BRE Digest 381 Site investigation of low rise buildings – trial pits

### Background

- CIRIA TN95 (1986) Proprietary trench support systems (microfiche only)
- Thorburn, S and Littlejohn, G S (1993) Underpinning and retention (Blackie)
- Bullivant, R and Bradbury, N W (1996) Underpinning: a practical guide (Blackwell)

### Classification

**CAWS** Group D,     **CEWS** Class C,F&P,     **CI/SfB** Code (1-)B

# Group C – Primary structure
## 1 – General concrete

Read the Introduction before using the following guidelines

## Scope

- Construction/maintenance/demolition procedures.
- Consideration of working at height or depth.
- Size of any pour, construction joints, expansion joints, movement joints and their positions.
- Element size/length/weight.
- Ducts, holes, chases, cutting, drilling.
- Falsework, formwork, shuttering.
- Bearings/connections/movement joints, water bars.
- Surface preparation, grit blasting, chemical retarders, expanded metal.
- Prefabrication – advantage, reduction of different activities.

## Exclusions

- Ornamental concrete.
- Gunite/shotcrete.
- Grout.

## Major hazards

Refer to the Introduction for details of accident types and health risks

**Falling from height**
Operatives falling during: preparation of falsework, formwork, concreting, curing.

**Health hazards**
Cement dust.
Wet concrete:
- skin/eye irritation,
- caustic burning.

**Noise and vibration**
Concrete:
- scabbling,
- breaking.

**Inhalation of dust**
Concrete :
- demolition,
- drilling/cutting,
- scabbling.

**Impact**
Concrete vibrators.
Concrete pumps.
Moving plant contact.
Skips, dumpers.

**Fumes/heat**
Cutting/thermic
lances:
- inhalation,
- burns.

# C1
## Group C – Primary structure
## 1 – General concrete

**A** — GENERAL PLANNING

**B** — EXCAVATIONS AND FOUNDATIONS

**C 1** — PRIMARY STRUCTURE

**D** — BUILDING ELEMENTS AND BUILDING SERVICES

**E 1** — CIVIL ENGINEERING

## Specific hazard identification

Possible key considerations:

- **Materials choice** – Show that concrete is the appropriate material.
- **Properties** – Can elements, properties, features be standardised to simplify working procedures?
- **Prefabrication** – Show off-site fabrication design has been maximised.
- **Procedure** – Show that material is being handled appropriately.
- **Materials** – When is the concrete deleterious to: skin, eyes, inhalation, ingestion?
- **Climate** – Show that effects will not be exacerbated by sun, wind, cold, heat or water.
- **Emissions** – Will the process cause: fire, fumes, spray, dust, toxins?
- **Protection** – Has the need for additional protection been identified: enclosure, extraction, isolation, personal protection?
- **Any others?**

## Prompts

- Location
- At height/depth
- Materials properties
- Element size
- Prefabrication
- Construction joints
- Holes/services
- Cutting
- Fixings
- Weight
- Demolition
- Access

## Hazards consideration in design

| Stage | Considerations and issues | Possible design options to avoid or mitigate hazards identified for general concrete |
|---|---|---|
| Concept Design | • Why use concrete?<br>• Scope of use<br>• Familiar?<br>  - materials<br>  - application<br>  - location<br>• Environment<br>• Materials<br>• Demand on resources | • Having chosen to use concrete, will it be identified where it will be mixed and placed? Can it be safely located in that position?<br>• If in-situ concrete, does the site have sufficient space for batching or is ready – mixed concrete available, within reasonable access to the point of placing?<br>• Is the way in which the material is to be used known to the proposed contractors?<br>• Will hazardous processes be required? eg hydrocutting, thermic lance |
| Scheme Design | • Technology known?<br>• Characteristics<br>• Complexity<br>• Programme<br>• Review<br>• Process<br>• Protection<br>• In-situ concrete<br>• Pre-cast concrete<br>• Pre-stressed concrete | • Are special concrete mixes being used and can they be supplied locally to the site?<br>• Consider the programme: where and when will the concreting be carried out?<br>  - outside or undercover?<br>  - in summer or winter?<br>• Will concreting be at ground level and units raised or lowered? or prepared and concreted at height or depth?<br>• Do sequences and finishes require scabbling? |
| Detail Design | • Elements<br>• Standardisation<br>• Features<br>• Holes/fixing<br>• Cutting<br>• Constituents<br>• Method<br>• Plan/control<br>• Testing<br>• Monitoring<br>• Analysing | • If the design requires a specific method of build, set it down for the contractor.<br>• A safe method of construction should be determined by the designer.<br>• Optimise standard unit details to minimise errors.<br>• Include details for relevant stages in the life of the concrete element, construction, use, maintenance and demolition, chases, fixings, conduits, etc.<br>• Chases or holes should be detailed to be cast into the unit and not cut or drilled later. |

# Group C – Primary structure
## 1 – General concrete

## Examples of risk mitigation (methods of solution)

|  | **ISSUE** | |
| --- | --- | --- |
| **ACTION** | **Concrete frame building** | **Working at height to install embedded fixing in RC element** |
| **Avoidance**<br>Design to avoid identified hazards but beware of introducing others | Avoid working at height by fabricating elements off-site. | Fixing installed in element off-site to avoid working at height. |
| **Reduction**<br>Design to reduce identified hazards but beware of increasing others | Element prefabricated (eg reinforcement).<br>Fabricate at ground level and lift. | (Does not apply if risk can be avoided) |
| **Control**<br>Design to provide acceptable safeguards for all remaining identified hazards | Provide information of element construction. | (Does not apply if risk can be avoided) |

## Examples of risk mitigation (issues addressed at different stages)

An existing bridge over a busy road is to be upgraded. The abutments are adequate but the concrete deck and beams need to be replaced. The major risk is working at height and restricted access.

| **Concept design** | **Scheme design** | **Detail design** |
| --- | --- | --- |
| Consider fabrication off-site to avoid site activities at height over the road. | The beams will be pre-cast concrete. Tee beams chosen to provide immediate access for operatives to the bridgedeck. | Pre-cast units to be designed with service ducts, street furniture fixings and temporary protection included, to avoid on-site activities. |

Concrete chambers are required to facilitate maintenance inspection of underground services. The variable ground conditions and limited working space indicate that working at depth within the excavations is a major risk.

| **Concept design** | **Scheme design** | **Detail design** |
| --- | --- | --- |
| Hazard studies have indicated that inspection chambers should be reinforced concrete to reduce hazardous activities in excavations, at depth. | To reduce hazards of depths, the inspection chambers will be pre-cast on-site and lowered into position. The additional hazards introduced by this method have been considered preferable to those being avoided. | Inspection pit design will include cast-in ducts, step irons, fixings, lifting points. |

**Side tabs:**
- A — GENERAL PLANNING
- B — EXCAVATIONS AND FOUNDATIONS
- C 1 — PRIMARY STRUCTURE
- D — BUILDING ELEMENTS AND BUILDING SERVICES
- E — CIVIL ENGINEERING

# Group C – Primary structure
## 1 – General concrete

A — GENERAL PLANNING

B — EXCAVATIONS AND FOUNDATIONS

C 1 — PRIMARY STRUCTURE

D — BUILDING ELEMENTS AND BUILDING SERVICES

E 1 — CIVIL ENGINEERING

## Related issues

References within this document

| References | Related issues |
| --- | --- |
| A1 | Surrounding environment for precautions to control spread of concrete materials. |
| A2 | Site clearance will need controls to prevent pollution from concrete dust. |
| A3 | Site investigation may be required to determine the extent and condition of the concrete. |
| A4 | Access onto the site will be carefully planned to transport concrete or the constituent materials. |
| A5 | Site layout will need to be co-ordinated with the requirement for concreting facilities. |
| C2 | Insitu concrete will need to consider this work sector. |
| C3 | Precast concrete will consider this work sector. |
| C4 | Prestressed concrete will consider this work sector. |
| D1 | External cladding may be made of concrete. |
| D5 | Surface coatings and finishes may be an application to concrete products. |
| D10 | Vertical transportation needs to be carefully considered when transporting concrete. |
| E1 | Civil engineering small works will most likely use concrete. |
| E2 | Roads, working adjacent to, maintenance. |
| E3 | Railways, working adjacent to, maintenance. |
| E4 | Bridge construction will probably use concrete. |
| E5 | Bridge maintenance will cover concrete elements. |
| E6 | Working over/near water may place concrete in an aggressive environment. |
| E7 | Cofferdams in water are likely to be concrete. |

## References for further guidance

Primary general references and background information given in Section 4

### Primary

- CIRIA R146 (1995) Design and construction of joints in concrete structures
- HSE HSG150 Health and safety in construction (2006)
- HSE CIS26 (revised) Cement
- BS 5975:1996 Code of practice for falsework (under revision)

### Secondary

- CIRIA PR70 (1999) How much noise do you make? A guide to assessing and managing noise on construction sites
- CIRIA R67 (1991) Tables of minimum striking times for soffit and vertical formwork
- CIRIA R136 (1995) Formwork striking times
- CIRIA SP57 (1988) Handling of materials on site
- HSE GS28 Parts 1 to 4 Safe erection of structures

### Background

- CIRIA C512 (2000) Environmental handbook for building and civil engineering projects Part 1: design and specification
- CIRIA R120 (1990) A guide to reducing the exposure of construction workers to noise
- British Cement Association (1993) Concrete on site (BCA)

### Classification

**CAWS**  Group E,  **CEWS**  Class F,G,H,  **CI/SfB**  Code (2-)q

Read the Introduction before using the following guidelines

A — GENERAL PLANNING
B — EXCAVATIONS AND FOUNDATIONS
C 2 — PRIMARY STRUCTURE
D — BUILDING ELEMENTS AND BUILDING SERVICES
E — CIVIL ENGINEERING

## Scope

- Falsework – scaffolding, patent structure, steelwork, timber.
- Formwork – temporary, permanent, erecting, striking, pour sizes, construction joints.
- Reinforcement – spacing, grouping, supporting, projecting.
- Positioning concrete – skips, pumps, barrows, shute, tremmie.
- Placing concrete – spreading, levelling, loading, finishing (power float/tamp etc.).
- Concrete compaction – vibrating poker, tamper, external vibrators.
- Striking formwork/falsework – concrete maturity.
- Temporary loading conditions – temporary design, temporary support.

## Exclusions

- No-fines concrete.
- Dry-lean concrete.
- Demolition.

## Major hazards

Refer to the Introduction for details of accident types and health risks

**Falls from height**
Accessing or working on scaffold, preparing for or placing in-situ concrete, access, working on formwork.

**Noise, vibration**
Working with breakers, vibrators, scabblers, saws, etc.

**Collapse**
Formwork/falsework permanent structure collapse under loading from fresh concrete, excessive spans, large sections.

**Moving Plant**
Collision with moving machines (concrete trucks, concrete mixers, pumps, dumpers, etc.).

**Health hazards**
Inhalation of dust from cement, breaking out or scabbling concrete.

**Irritants**
Concrete constituent materials, mould oils:
- skin/eye irritation
- caustic burns.

# Group C – Primary structure
## 2 – In-situ concrete

**C2**

A — GENERAL PLANNING

B — EXCAVATIONS AND FOUNDATIONS

C2 — PRIMARY STRUCTURE

D — BUILDING ELEMENTS AND BUILDING SERVICES

E — CIVIL ENGINEERING

I

## Specific hazard identification

**Possible key considerations:**

- **Conditions** – Where are all the temporary and permanent conditions listed?
- **Design** – How is it shown that the element is designed to satisfy all the temporary and permanent conditions?
- **Temporary works** – Demonstrate how hazards have been checked in falsework and formwork design.
- **Access** – Show adequate access for plant, materials and operatives has been identified.
- **Space** – Show there is adequate space for access and working.
- **Environment** – Demonstrate the working environment is satisfactory.
- **Work Access** – Where is access to work areas set out?
- **Storage** – Show that materials storage areas have been considered.
- **Prefabrication** – Show that prefabrication has been maximised.
- **Any others?**

## Prompts

- Access
- Transporting materials
- Positioning materials
- Formwork/falsework
- Pour sizes
- Construction joints
- Reinforcement
- Concreting
- Compaction
- Protection
- Loading

## Hazards consideration in design

| Stage | Considerations and issues | Possible design options to avoid or mitigate hazards identified for insitu concrete |
|---|---|---|
| Concept design | • Why in-situ concrete?<br>• Scope of work<br>• Overall mass<br>• Familiar to use<br>• Accessibility set out<br>• Interfaces defined<br>• Characteristics | • Can the in-situ concrete work be safely constructed in the time available or should alternatives be considered (eg pre-cast concrete)?<br>• Does the in-situ concrete work constitute a significant part of the work? If the in-situ work is not extensive, avoid sophisticated details.<br>• Avoid using in-situ concrete at height or depth if possible. |
| Scheme design | • Programme plan<br>• Temporary works<br>• Review complexity<br>• Span/section defined<br>• Sequence planned<br>• Temporary loading<br>• Tolerances set out<br>• Protection defined<br>• Procedures set down<br>• Falsework design<br>• Formwork design | • Use a design that allows for adequate access to construct the element on site, given selected production methods.<br>• Will the formwork for the site concreting be open and accessible, or restricted and congested?<br>• If the design assumes a specific construction (and demolition) sequence of build, identify it clearly in the design.<br>• Inform formwork/falsework designer of element design assumptions.<br>• Specify sequences and finishes that do not require scabbling. |
| Detail design | • Access planned<br>• Formwork detail<br>• Falsework detail<br>• Reinforcement<br>• Pour sequence<br>• Pour sizes<br>• Curing/maturity<br>• Striking criteria<br>• Testing materials | • Ensure that it is possible to have safe access and place of work to construct the element.<br>• Reinforcement cages or mats should be rigid. Avoid congestion of reinforcement in an element.<br>• Identify reasonable pour layouts/sizes, with only reinforcement lap lengths protruding from the pour.<br>• If the design assumes a depropping/striking time criterion (strike before/not until), ensure that it is clearly identified for the contractor in the health and safety plan.<br>• Form chases and holes to avoid cutting or drilling later. |

## Examples of risk mitigation (methods of solution)

| ACTION \ ISSUE | Site activities | Surface preparation |
|---|---|---|
| **Avoidance**<br>Design to avoid identified hazards but beware of introducing others | Avoid working in confined areas. | Avoid scabbling by co-ordinating construction joints and reinforcement arrangement. |
| **Reduction**<br>Design to reduce identified hazards but beware of increasing others | Simplify and standardise details. | Specify use of surface retarders for joint preparation. |
| **Control**<br>Design to provide acceptable safeguards for all remaining identified hazards | | |

A | GENERAL PLANNING
B | EXCAVATIONS AND FOUNDATIONS
C2 | PRIMARY STRUCTURE
D | BUILDING ELEMENTS AND BUILDING SERVICES
E | CIVIL ENGINEERING

## Examples of risk mitigation (issues addressed at different stages)

A framed building is to be constructed on a congested site. The frame is not a regular grid; spans and loading vary. One option is to design for a reinforced concrete frame founded on a continuous raft.

| Concept design | Scheme design | Detail design |
|---|---|---|
| Concept reviews indicate that an in-situ concrete structure is the simplest form of construction for this irregular building, thus reducing hazards. | Design to standardise beam/slab column sizes wherever possible. Reinforcement details and construction joints planned to suit shutter assembly on site. | The specification requires the construction joint preparation to be carried out using a surface retarder to reduce noise and dust hazards from concrete surface preparation. |

A reinforced concrete retaining wall is being built along the side of a road in a town centre as part of a road improvement scheme. Earlier considerations indicate that insitu concrete is the preferred option. The retaining wall has to be founded at depth in order to reach ground with sufficient bearing capacity. The design will need to take into consideration the difficult working conditions to be encountered on site in close proximity to a busy road.

| Concept design | Scheme design | Detail design |
|---|---|---|
| The design will reduce the hazards on site by minimising and separating the number of activities required to be carried out at depth. | Reinforcement and formwork will be fabricated off-site, delivered in panels at the surface and lowered into position, to reduce activities at depth. | Control procedures will be required to monitor air quality in the excavation, which will be affected by traffic exhaust gases. |

## Related issues

References within this document

| References | Related issues |
|---|---|
| A1 | Surrounding environment will need to be considered when examining access to the pour location. |
| A2 | Site clearance and simple demolition may be relevant in order that in-situ concreting activities can proceed. |
| A3 | Site investigation may have to be carried out before the criteria for the design of the reinforced concrete works can be established. |
| A4 | Access on the site will need to be determined to ensure the safe construction of the in-situ concrete. |
| A5 | Site layout intersects with decisions to use in-situ concrete. |
| B2 | Deep basements shafts are likely to use in-situ concrete construction. |
| B4 | Retaining walls are likely to use in-situ concrete construction. |
| B6 | Piling should be considered, as bored piling will use in-situ concrete construction. |
| B7 | Under-pinning works will use in-situ concrete construction. |
| C1 | General concrete |
| C3 | Pre-cast concrete may be considered as an alternative to in-situ reinforced concrete. |
| C4 | Pre-stressed, post-tensioned concrete may be also considered as an alternative to reinforced concrete. |
| E1 | Civil engineering, small works are likely to be using in-situ reinforced concrete structures. |
| E4 | Bridge construction may well be constructed in in-situ reinforced concrete. |
| E5 | Bridge maintenance will probably require periodic attention to in-situ concrete details. |
| E6 | Working over/near water is likely to use in-situ concrete. |
| E7 | Cofferdams in water may use in-situ concrete. |

## References for further guidance

Primary general references and background information given in Section 4

### Primary

- HSE HSG150 Health and safety in construction
- HSE CIS26 (revised) Cement
- BS 5975:1996 Code of practice for falsework
- BS EN 13374:2004 Temporary edge protection systems

### Secondary

- HSE GS28 Parts 1 to 4 Safe erection of structures
- CIRIA R67 (1991) Tables of minimum striking times for soffit and vertical formwork
- CIRIA R136 (1995) Formwork striking times
- CIRIA R108 (1985) Concrete pressure on formwork
- CIRIA SP57 (1988) Handling of materials on site
- CIRIA C558 (2001) Permanent formwork in construction
- Concrete Society CS123 Checklist for erecting and dismantling falsework
- Concrete Society CS144 Checklist for assembly , use and striking of formwork

### Background

- CIRIA SP118 (1995) Steel reinforcement

### Classification

**CAWS** Group E, **CEWS** Class F, **CI/SfB** Code (2-)E

Read the Introduction before using the following guidelines

## Scope

- Pre-cast work on site – cast adjacent to final location.
- Pre-cast work offsite – resultant effect of pre-cast construction decisions on the site.
- Transportation – from off-site pre-cast yard to construction site.
- Lifting – during fabrication, transportation, installation.
- Positioning – setting out, tolerances, locating, securing.
- Bearings/supports – adequacy, stability, temporary works.
- Fixings and holes/openings for handrails, ladders, barriers, services, chases.
- Finishes – to avoid site preparatory activities.
- Temporary loading, supporting, propping, bracing.

## Exclusions

- Railway works (see E3).
- Marine works.
- Pre-stressed concrete (see C4).
- Cladding panels (see D1).

## Major hazards

Refer to the Introduction for details of accident types and health risks

**Falling from height**
Operatives falling while accessing, locating or fixing pre-cast units.

**Crushing**
Lifting procedure for unit not defined in design:
-     adequate lifting points
-     maturity of concrete at lifting.

**Collapse:**
Pre-cast unit unable to carry loading or insufficiently restrained in temporary condition.

**Collapse**
Units placed in wrong position (inverted or on their side or located with incorrect bearing).

**Collapse:**
Pre-cast composite units may fail if not propped to carry the in-situ topping and temporary load.

**Handling**
Pre-cast unit is a shape/weight that is difficult to transport, lift or position.

A   GENERAL PLANNING

B   EXCAVATIONS AND FOUNDATIONS

C 3   PRIMARY STRUCTURE

D   BUILDING ELEMENTS AND BUILDING SERVICES

E I   CIVIL ENGINEERING

## Specific hazard identification

**Possible key considerations:**

- **Tolerance control** – encourages rapid and safe assembly.
- **Work at height** – Where are critical considerations?
- **Temporary conditions** – Are the assumed temporary conditions set down? Show that it is designed for fabrication, lifting, transport placing, temporary loading, etc.
- **Installation** – Do the units require installation procedures that are not likely to be routine on site?
- **Procedures** – Ensure that the procedures described for unit installation are sufficiently comprehensive.
- **Insitu stitch** – Where are details of in-situ infills or topping?
- **Any others?**

## Prompts

- Access/transport
- Mock-up
- Handling points
- Unit weights
- Lifting procedures
- Transporting
- Positioning
- Temporary support
- Composite action
- Orientation
- Demolition
- Training

## Hazards consideration in design

| Stage | Considerations and issues | Possible design options to avoid or mitigate hazards identified for pre-cast concrete |
|---|---|---|
| Concept design | • Why pre-cast?<br>• Scope of work<br>• Familiarly used?<br>• Define accessibility<br>• Interfaces set out<br>• Sequence defined<br>• Overall mass<br>• Technology known | • Do the pre-cast concrete elements form an insignificant part of the work? Are they to be cast on site? If so, try to ensure details are simple.<br>• Clearly define the designers' intended construction sequence<br>• Are the units large? Can they be easily transported and handled and positioned on site?<br>• Can pre-cast units be easily and safely positioned in their likely location? |
| Scheme design | • Pre-stressed?<br>• Unit characteristics<br>• Span/section known<br>• Shape identified<br>• Number of units<br>• Loading condition<br>• Protection defined<br>• Tolerances set out<br>• Procedures defined | • Is the pre-cast supplier likely to have made similar units previously?<br>• Ensure that the limits of size, weight and number are known by all parties as soon as possible.<br>• Specify how the units are to be protected, handled, lifted and positioned. Include lifting points.<br>• Ideally the units should be lifted and finally located direct from their transporter. |
| Detail design | • Handling designed<br>• Handling formwork and rein-forcement<br>• Surface treatment<br>• Cutting/sawing<br>• Inserts/fixings<br>• Positioning/locate<br>• Temporary support | • Ensure that all holes, chases, conduits, fixings, etc. are cast into the precast unit.<br>• Ensure that detailing of reinforcement cages provides for easy lifting. Identify lifting points.<br>• Minimise and simplify locating and fixing procedures and details especially at height or depth. |

## Examples of risk mitigation (methods of solution)

| ISSUE<br><br>ACTION | Element design | Connections/tolerances |
|---|---|---|
| **Avoidance**<br>Design to avoid identified hazards but beware of introducing others | Standardise unit size and shape. | Simplify unit shape for tolerance control. |
| **Reduction**<br>Design to reduce identified hazards but beware of increasing others | Consider limit for unit size/shape/weight. | Simplify lifting fixing/connection details. |
| **Control**<br>Design to provide acceptable safeguards for all remaining identified hazards | Detail unit handling procedures/training. | Specify location/ connection procedures. |

## Examples of risk mitigation (issues addressed at different stages)

Apartment blocks on a site are required to be built within a short site construction period. To achieve the programme and budget, it has been decided to maximise the off-site fabrication process. One option is the use of pre-cast concrete for structural elements.

| Concept design | Scheme design | Detail design |
|---|---|---|
| Pre-cast construction, judged to allow greater standardisation – avoids hazards of complicated in-situ details and work on site. | Standardise units where possible. Consider dimensions, weight and shape of units. Design for loads during lifting. | To reduce handling and fixing hazards, the pre-cast units will include cast-in connections for handling, positioning, hand rails and running lines |

An office block is to be built over vaulted arches which are to be retained. The columns for the offices pass through the vaulting and are founded below the vaults. Due to lack of headroom in the vaults and high loading, the foundations are proposed to be hand-dug caissons with an option to use pre-cast segmental rings as liners.

| Concept design | Scheme design | Detail design |
|---|---|---|
| This application of caissons is not a familiar technique. Designers are examining the pre-cast liner option in order to avoid hazards of collapse. | A design study determines that a 3 segment pre-cast concrete liner reduces hazards over the in-situ option. | Mock-up trials indicated pre-cast liner segments should include lifting sockets, grout/water seals, grouting and vent tubes and escape ladder fixings. |

## Related issues

References within this document

| References | Related issues |
|---|---|
| A1 | Surrounding environment will need to be considered with regard to transporting and positioning pre-cast units. |
| A2 | Site clearance may be required in order to prepare for access and positioning of pre-cast units. |
| A3 | Site investigation could be required in order to finalise which elements are pre-cast. |
| A4 | Access will be required for the transportation, positioning and placing (or removal) of the unit. |
| A5 | Site layout will interact with access, positioning and placing of pre-cast units. |
| B1 | General excavations could entail the use of pre-cast units. Ensure they will resist the conditions. |
| B2 | Deep basements/shafts may use pre-cast units as lining in segmental form for retaining structures. |
| B3 | Trenches for foundations and services, pre-cast units may be used to carry services. |
| B4 | Retaining walls – may be pre-cast concrete. |
| B6 | Piling – may use pre-cast concrete for driven piles. |
| C1 | General concrete – ensure the pre-cast units perform adequately. |
| C2 | In-situ concrete may be considered as an alternative for pre-cast concrete. |
| C4 | Pre-stressed, post-tensioned concrete may be pre-cast concrete. |
| D1 | External cladding likely to be pre-cast if it is to be made of concrete. |
| E1 | Civil engineering, small works will frequently use pre-cast concrete units. |
| E4 | Bridge construction may be entirely or partly pre-cast concrete. |
| E5 | Bridge maintenance could entail the maintenance of pre-cast concrete units and the sealing, joints etc. |
| E6 | Working or near water could use pre-cast concrete. |

## References for further guidance

Primary general references and background information given in Section 4

### Primary

- CIRIA TN137 (1991) Selection and use of fixings in concrete and masonry (microfiche)
- CIRIA SP57 (1988) Handling of materials on site
- Precast Concrete Frame Association: Code of practice for safe erection of pre-cast concrete frameworks (1999)
- CIRIA C703 (2003) Crane stability on site
- CIRIA C654 (2006) Tower crane stability

### Secondary

- BS 5975:1996 Code of practice for falsework
- CIRIA TN104 (1981) Pre-cast concrete tunnel linings
- HSE GS28 Parts 1 to 4 Safe erection of structures

### Background

- BS 7121: Code of Practice for safe use of cranes [several parts]
- Elliott, K S (2002) Precast concrete structures (Butterworth-Heinemann)
- Elliott, K S (1996) Multi-storey precast concrete framed structures (Blackwell)

### Classification

**CAWS** Group E, **CEWS** Class H, **CI/SfB** Code (2-)f

# Group C – Primary structure
## 4 – Pre-stressed, post-tensioned concrete

C4

Read the Introduction before using the following guidelines

## Scope

- Post-tensioned reinforced concrete.
- Reinforcement – span, anchor zones, duct supports.
- Stressing ducts – gauge, profile, fixing, jointing.
- Stressing cables – wires, strands.
- Anchorage zones – anchor blocks, wedges, jacks.
- Grouting – grouting tubes, venting, duct profiles.
- Stressing procedure – when, sequence, linear, monitor, precautions.
- Materials – concrete maturity, strength, creep, shrinkage.
- Demolition.

**Special notes:**

1. Stresses used in pre-stressed concrete are usually very high. Care must be taken in design and use of all materials

2. Wire = single

   Strand = multi-wire

   Tendon = multi strand

## Exclusions

- Pre-stessed pre-tensioned concrete.
- Externally post-tensioned structures eg silos, bridges.
- Pre-stressed non-reinforcement concrete structures eg. ground anchors.

## Major hazards

Refer to the Introduction for details of accident types and health risks

**Falls from height**
Operatives fall from access/ elements during fixing/ stressing.

**Collapse/crushing**
Units unstable in temporary condition (high d/b ratio).

**Impact/collapse**
Strand breakages during stressing:
- strand damage or duct obstruction/defect
- duct alignment.

**Inadequate access**
Operatives unable safely to access work area, poor materials handling facilities.

**Collapse**
Duct breaks loose and floats during concreting (duct support failure).

**Impact/collapse**
Collapse of element during demolition. Inadequate support and failure of compression zone during demolition.

## Specific hazard identification

**Possible key considerations:**

- **Assumptions** – Where are the design assumptions stated clearly?
- **Materials** – How will materials be maintained in good condition on site?
- **Access** – Show that the design will allow sufficient working space.
- **Design** – Show that the design avoids strand, anchor, reinforcement congestion.
- **Support** – Provide adequate support for stressing ducts.
- **Grouting** – Check grout vents are to be at highest point of duct profile.
- **Ducts** – How are stressing ducts kept clear of obstructions and water?
- **Strands** – Ensure strands are not snagged in ducts.
- **Any others?**

## Prompts

- Protect materials
- Access for fixing
- Access for stressing
- Stressing protection
- Grouting procedure
- Handling points
- Transportation
- Demolition

## Hazards consideration in design

| Stage | Considerations and issues | Possible design options to avoid or mitigate hazards identified for pre-stressed concrete |
|---|---|---|
| Concept design | • Why pre-stress?<br>• Scope of work<br>• Plan accessibility<br>• Define interfaces<br>• Sequence assumed<br>• Overall mass<br>• Technology known? | • Pre-stressing can be hazardous if inadequate design guidance to the contractor.<br>• Loads and stresses are high – more easily controlled in a factory? Are the elements to be made on site?<br>• Will the necessary construction expertise be locally available to the site? |
| Scheme design | • Unit characteristics<br>• Span section review<br>• Number of units<br>• Loading conditions<br>• Locate tendons<br>• Anchorage access<br>• Duct support<br>• Stressing protection<br>• Tolerances defined | • Units should be standardised wherever possible.<br>• Prepare the design so that it allows the work to be carried out on site in good working conditions.<br>• Ensure that the design sequence allows the contractor to provide good access.<br>• Design and detail to reduce the risk that the materials will be damaged prior to or during installation (eg to reduce ad hoc repair work on site). |
| Detail design | • Procedures defined<br>• Care of materials<br>• Tendon layout<br>• Duct profile, radii, joints, vents<br>• Anchorage layout<br>• Strands replaced<br>• Stressing sequence<br>• Grouting sequence<br>• Striking supports<br>• Deflection/creep<br>• Loading application | • Specify conditions for materials storage, dry, well laid-out, clean, secure, etc.<br>• Be aware of strand installation method when designing ducts.<br>• Design duct supports.<br>• Ensure adequate spacing for anchorages.<br>• Avoid dead-end anchorages.<br>• Specify installation procedures and controlled inspections of work.<br>• Specify protection of materials, installation and completed work.<br>• Detail control procedures prior to, during and after tendon stressing to reduce risk of hazards occurring. |

## Examples of risk mitigation (methods of solution)

| ISSUE<br><br>ACTION | Reduce and simplify site activities | Cable failure during post-tensioning |
|---|---|---|
| **Avoidance**<br>Design to avoid identified hazards but beware of introducing others | Pre-construct off-site or at ground level. | Avoid stressing duct congestion. |
| **Reduction**<br>Design to reduce identified hazards but beware of increasing others | Pre-stressed proposals simplified and good access provided. | Smooth stressing duct profile. |
| **Control**<br>Design to provide acceptable safeguards for all remaining identified hazards | Outline competence level required and highlight the need to co-ordinate with concurrent trades. | Outline stressing procedures. |

Side tabs:
- A — GENERAL PLANNING
- B — EXCAVATIONS AND FOUNDATIONS
- C 4 — PRIMARY STRUCTURE
- D — BUILDING ELEMENTS AND BUILDING SERVICES
- E — CIVIL ENGINEERING

## Examples of risk mitigation (issues addressed at different stages)

A building constructed in the 1930s has undergone change of use to offices. This requires a review of the existing rivetted steel frame.

| Concept design | Scheme design | Detail design |
|---|---|---|
| To carry additional loading, it requires long span plated steel beams to be upgraded. The beams will be cased in reinforced concrete and post-tensioned in order to carry the new floor loading. | The composite post-tensioned solution avoids hazards of gas cutting and welding, while minimising noise and dust | Provide relevant information to Planning Supervisor for sequence of working and design assumptions. |

The ramp beams are to be built for an elevated road deck. Due to alignment, the elevated ramp structure is complex and the design needs to reduce the hazards of congested construction at height.

The geometry of the beams are complex due to curved alignment on plan and elevation. The beam depth will be restricted by headroom constraints below them.

| Concept design | Scheme design | Detail design |
|---|---|---|
| The ramp beams for an elevated road deck are to be cast in-situ post-tensioned concrete, instead of pre-cast, in order to avoid difficult details of casting PC units, but will now involve increased work at height. | The in-situ design has avoided the hazards associated with complex layout of stressing tendons. | To reduce hazards, details provide adequate spacing of anchor blocks in relation to stressing jack requirements. |

**A** GENERAL PLANNING

**B** EXCAVATIONS AND FOUNDATIONS

**C 4** PRIMARY STRUCTURE

**D** BUILDING ELEMENTS AND BUILDING SERVICES

**E I** CIVIL ENGINEERING

## Related issues

References within this document

| References | Related issues |
|---|---|
| A1 | Surrounding environment may have to be considered for stressing procedures and protection. |
| A2 | Site clearance and simple demolition will need to identify those elements that are post-tensioned. |
| A3 | Site investigation may be required to determine the extent and details of pre-stressed concrete within a structure. |
| A4 | Access on the site will need to consider location and access to pre-stressed units. |
| A5 | Site layout will need to identify the positioning of pre-stressed units, to design access and protection. |
| B4 | Retaining walls may be designed with the use of pre-stressed concrete, (pre-tensioned or post-tensioned). |
| B5 | Ground stabilisation may be carried out with the use of ground anchors (in effect, a form of post-tensioned concrete). |
| C1 | General concrete will identify the constituents of the concrete in the pre-stressed member. |
| C2 | In-situ concrete – Post-tensioned unit is more likely to be cast in-situ (in position). |
| C3 | Pre-cast concrete – The post-tensioned units may be pre-cast prior to final location. |
| D7-D10 | Services – Extreme caution should be exercised if services require the formation of builders work openings in pre-stressed units. They should all be pre-formed prior to concreting. Never cut on site. |
| E1-E8 | Civil engineering works – Pre-stressed concrete frequently occurs in civil engineering works. |
| E4 | Bridge construction is often pre-stressed concrete. |
| E5 | Bridge maintenance should always check pre-stressed members during condition surveys. |
| E6 | Working over/near water may use pre-stressed concrete. |

## References for further guidance

Primary general references and background information given in Section 4

### Primary

- HSE GS49 Pre-stressed concrete
- CIRIA SP57 (1988) Handling of materials on site

### Secondary

- CIRIA R28 (1971) The connection of pre-cast concrete structural members (microfiche)
- CIRIA TN129 (1987) Prestressed concrete beams – Controlled demolition and pre-stress loss assessment
- HSG 150 Health and safety in construction
- HSE INDG258 Safe work in confined spaces

### Background

- BS 5975:1996 Code of practice for falsework
- Hurst, M K (1998) Prestressed concrete. 2nd ed (Spon)

### Classification

**CAWS** Group E, **CEWS** Class H, **CI/SfB** Code (2-)E

Read the Introduction before using the following guidelines

## Scope

- Building frames such as offices, schools, hotels, etc.
- Portal frames for agricultural or industrial premises.
- Towers and chimneys, assembled on site.
- Footbridges and other load carrying spans.
- Gantries for street signs/lighting and other similar.
- Atria or other facades based on a structural steel frame.
- Hot-rolled and cold-formed sections.

## Exclusions

- Temporary works.
- Stability during erection (see C6).
- Corrosion/fire protection (see D5).
- Stressed skin designs.
- Cable tied and fabric structures.

## Major hazards

Refer to the Introduction for details of accident types and health risks

**Falls from Height**
Placing, stability and provision of working platforms, access.

**Collapse**
Storage areas, stacking and stability, falling objects, access, temporary bracing.

**Hazardous operations**
Cutting/Welding.
Painting.
Descaling.

**Mobile Plant**
Delivery, traffic control, offloading, slinging.
Site routes.

**Moving objects**
Remedial works, plumbing, levelling.
Trapping.
Manual handling.

**Noise, vibration**
Bolting, drilling.
Reaming.

**A** GENERAL PLANNING

**B** EXCAVATIONS AND FOUNDATIONS

**C 5** PRIMARY STRUCTURE

**D** BUILDING ELEMENTS AND BUILDING SERVICES

**E** CIVIL ENGINEERING

A **GENERAL PLANNING**

B **EXCAVATIONS AND FOUNDATIONS**

C 5 **PRIMARY STRUCTURE**

D **BUILDING ELEMENTS AND BUILDING SERVICES**

E I **CIVIL ENGINEERING**

## Specific hazard identification

**Possible key considerations:**

- **Delivery** – How will pieces be manoeuvred to and onto site?
- **Logistics** – How will delivery match sequence of use?
- **Lifting** – What are the requirements to allow the (tower) crane driver the facility to lift and position the pieces safely?
- **Storage** – Where and how will items be stored as they are unloaded?
- **Stability** – When unloaded, how will stability of the pieces be controlled?
- **Access** – How will hand and power tools be used at the work site?
- **Working at height** – How will working at height be accomplished?
- **Light and air** – What sorts of local environments are involved?
- **Other activities** – How could the works affect other people? How might the workforce be affected by what is going on around them?
- **Any others?**

## Prompts

- Lifting
- Access
- Transport
- Positioning
- Alignment and fit-up
- Reaming
- Slotted holes
- Connection type
- Corrosion protection
- Welding
- Cutting
- Bolting
- Painting

## Hazards consideration in design

| Stage | Considerations and issues | Possible design options to avoid or mitigate hazards identified for general steelwork |
|---|---|---|
| Concept design | • Why use steelwork?<br>• Scope of work<br>• Element sizes<br>• Piece weights<br>• Manoeuvrability<br>• Equipment<br>• Site Environment | • Exploit the facility to quickly erect and achieve stability; a safe working platform offers specific safety advantages.<br>• Determine how the steel frame can provide working platforms for subsequent work and other trades.<br>• Assess methods for delivery, storage, pre-assembly and erection of steelwork to safeguard construction workers.<br>• Metal decking for composite slabs offers significant safety advantages during construction (eg stabilises the structure, provides safe working platform). |
| Scheme design | • Programme<br>• Craneage<br>• Working area<br>• Sub assemblies<br>• Movement joints<br>• Temporary loads<br>• Interface connections<br>• Sequencing of work | • Show how structure might be built to anticipate and eliminate (if possible) hazards.<br>• Consider how temporary/erection loads can be accommodated without the need for additional members or framing.<br>• Explore how pre-assembly off and on site can enhance health and safety.<br>• Consider installing staircases earlier to provide safer access.<br>• Ensure adequate bracing is provided as the frame is erected |
| Detail design | • Connection types<br>• Bolt types<br>• Temporary conditions<br>• Pre-assembly<br>• Lining and levelling<br>• Tolerances<br>• Painting<br>• Testing | • Consider advantages of repetition (eg one size, fully-threaded bolts) to reduce complexity of hazardous work.<br>• Ensure that connections are dimensionally tolerant to avoid need for remedial works at height.<br>• De-burr holes and grind arrises to make components safer to handle.<br>• Eliminate/reduce need for work on site at height by ensuring an adequate base is prepared to allow safe working of mechanical lifting plant.<br>• Avoid complex connections. |

## Examples of risk mitigation (methods of solution)

| ACTION | ISSUE | |
|---|---|---|
| | **Moving and storing materials** | **Working at height** |
| **Avoidance** Design to avoid identified hazards but beware of introducing others | Place steelwork straight from the lorry | Consider pre-assembly on the ground |
| **Reduction** Design to reduce identified hazards but beware of increasing others | Establish site to provide adequate laydown areas away from site traffic | Design-in lifting points and/or methods to release crane hooks remotely. |
| **Control** Design to provide acceptable safeguards for all remaining identified hazards | Use guys and timbers to support steelwork until placed in position | Incorporate safety harness attachment points in detailing |

## Examples of risk mitigation (issues addressed at different stages)

For a large portal frame warehouse, the designer wants to provide access within the building envelope for other works while the steel frame is being erected and before the building is clad and finally braced.

| Concept design | Scheme design | Detail design |
|---|---|---|
| A sequence of construction is designed so that other trades can rapidly follow on behind steelwork erection; bracing provided so that structural stability always maintained. | A method of pre-assembly and erection is established to ensure that the contractor can be advised of a way in which it can be built safely. | Baseplates and foundation are detailed to provide adequate resistance to overturning, by using four bolts to accommodate temporary conditions. |

A building refurbishment project involves the retention of a listed facade and the reconstruction of part of the building to link up to a 1930s steel-framed structure.

| Concept design | Scheme design | Detail design |
|---|---|---|
| Member serial sizes and lengths are kept down to a size which can be "threaded" into the structure without requiring a tower crane. | Bolted connections are adopted throughout because of the problem of welding in confined spaces with a lot of adjacent activity. | Connections are designed to be dimensionally tolerant, so that risk of misfit is minimised. |

Side tabs:

A GENERAL PLANNING

B EXCAVATIONS AND FOUNDATIONS

C 5 PRIMARY STRUCTURE

D BUILDING ELEMENTS AND BUILDING SERVICES

E CIVIL ENGINEERING

**A** GENERAL PLANNING

**B** EXCAVATIONS AND FOUNDATIONS

**C 5** PRIMARY STRUCTURE

**D** BUILDING ELEMENTS AND BUILDING SERVICES

**E I** CIVIL ENGINEERING

## Related issues

References within this document

| References | Related issues |
|---|---|
| A1 | Surrounding environment will need to be considered when examining access to deliver steelwork. |
| A2 | Site clearance and simple demolition may be needed so that steelwork storage and placing activities can proceed. |
| A4 | Access on the site will need to be determined to ensure the safe construction. |
| A5 | Site layout may interact with the decision to use steelwork, particularly if pre-assembly is used more generally. |
| C1 | General concrete is usually used for foundations for steelwork. |
| C6 | Temporary stability is a dominant issue when considering safe design in steelwork. |
| D3 | Atria are invariably designed in steelwork with glazing infill. |
| D5 | Surface coatings and finishes will always be required on exposed steelwork. |
| D10 | Lifts and travelators could have steel framing or have steelwork linking it to a concrete core. |
| E4 | Bridge construction may be steel and always has health and safety considerations. |
| E5 | Bridge maintenance will probably require periodic attention to steelwork. |
| E6 | Working over/near water may use any steelwork. |
| E7 | Cofferdams in water may use steelwork. |

## References for further guidance

Primary general references and background information given in Section 4

### Primary

- HSE GS28 Parts 1 to 4 Safe erection of structures
  - Part 1 Initial planning and design
  - Part 2 Site management and procedures
  - Part 3 Working places and access
  - Part 4 Legislation and training
- CIRIA C703 (2003) Crane stability on site
- CIRIA C654 (2006) Tower crane stability
- CIRIA SP57 (1988) Handling of materials on site

### Secondary

- SCI (2003) Steel Designers' Manual. 6th ed (Blackwell)
- CIRIA R87 (1981) Lack of fit in steel structures

### Background

- BS 5950 Structural use of steelwork [several parts]
- BS 7121 Code of Practice for safe use of cranes [several parts]
- BS EN 1263 Safety nets

### Classification

**CAWS** Group G, **CEWS** Class M, **CI/SfB** Code (28)h2

Read the Introduction before using the following guidelines

## Scope

- Site pre-assembly.
- Pre or part erection.
- Temporary works.
- Interim connections.
- Erection stability.
- Plumbing and levelling.
- Temporary bracing.
- Structural cores.
- Interfaces with other trades.
- Connections.

## Exclusions

- Temporary storage or laydown.
- Launched structures.
- Stressed skin designs.
- Cable tied and fabric structures.
- Demolition.

## Major hazards

Refer to the Introduction for details of accident types and health risks

**Falls from height**
Placing, stability and provision of working platforms, access.

**Collapse**
Excessive loading or load reversal.
Inadequate ties, struts or bracing.
Incorrect sequence.
Incomplete assembly.

**Noise vibration**
Pneumatic and manual wrenches and hammers.

**Harmful Substances**
Sparks and heat from burning and welding.
Electricity
Paints, greases etc.

**Moving objects/trappings**
Placing of steelwork. Closure of joints.
Sharp objects.
Baseplate packing.

**Refer also to Sector C5 hazards**

GENERAL PLANNING   **A**

EXCAVATIONS AND FOUNDATIONS   **B**

PRIMARY STRUCTURE   **C 6**

BUILDING ELEMENTS AND BUILDING SERVICES   **D**

CIVIL ENGINEERING   **E**

## Specific hazard identification

**Possible key considerations:**

- **Handling** – How are units to be brought together/ assembled?
- **Assembly** – What different methods of assembly are safest for this site?
- **Buildability** – Determine at an early stage how the structure might be built safely. Repeatedly reconsider this as design proceeds to ensure that safety is maintained or enhanced.
- **Structural Capacity** – Which methods and sequences of assembly could inadvertently lead to overloading?
- **Stability Core** – If any parts of the structure rely upon other particular parts for their stability, is this obvious?
- **Site Condition** – What site conditions could affect these works? How can these be designed out?
- **Pieces (and bundles) of steel** could have their weight marked and locations and orientations shown, making placement easier.
- **Manoeuvring** – Once on the crane hook, do loads need additional control? How will this be provided?
- **Any others?**

## Prompts

- Local access
- Visibility
- Ground stability
- Surrounding environment
- Confined spaces
- Temporary guys/struts
- Alignment
- Special connections
- Corrosion protection
- Welding
- Cutting
- Loose fit pieces
- Cleaning and painting
- Checking and testing
- Base grouting

## Hazards consideration in design

| Stage | Considerations and issues | Possible design options to avoid or mitigate hazards identified for stability and erection of structural steelwork |
|---|---|---|
| Concept design | • Scope of work<br>• Form of construction<br>• Building shape/size<br>• Pre-assembly<br>• Sequences<br>• Major Plant | • Because the highest incidence of accident and injuries arise from "falls from height" this must be a special consideration when considering ways to allow safe work on partially-erected steel frames.<br>• Consider sequence of site/structure development to determine the most appropriate option. |
| Scheme design | • Site access<br>• Craneage<br>• Ground conditions<br>• Work sequences<br>• Sub-assemblies<br>• Element sizes/weights<br>• Temporary loads<br>• Work platforms<br>• Inter-connections | • Can the steel frame erection be conceived as inherently stable sub-assemblies?<br>• Consider if welding, HSFG, or bolts in bearing offer any particular health and safety benefits – eg by providing temporary moment capacity.<br>• Assess structure to see if areas can be rapidly developed to act as stable work platforms.<br>• Design so that stairways can be installed ahead of frame erection, for safer access. |
| Detail design | • Connection details<br>• Lot sizes and sequences<br>• Column bases<br>• Temporary storage<br>• Bolt types and sizes<br>• Tightening and torquing<br>• Tolerances | • For ease of erection, seek to use fewer – or even one – size of bolt throughout.<br>• Can elements in tension also be designed to accept temporary compression loads (to provide enhanced stability)?<br>• Ensure that structural mechanism assumed for method of construction is communicated to all who might need to know.<br>• Include temporary working platforms and/or harness attachment points. |

## Examples of risk mitigation (methods of solution)

| ACTION \ ISSUE | Assembly stability | Making connections |
|---|---|---|
| **Avoidance**<br>Design to avoid identified hazards but beware of introducing others | Design for assembly at ground level and to have fewer but larger lifts. Ensure provision of base for cranage. | Adopt positive seating systems. Explore range of connection types. |
| **Reduction**<br>Design to reduce identified hazards but beware of increasing others | Outline sequence of construction which allows in-built stability. | Specify one size, fully-threaded free running bolts to simplify work at height. |
| **Control**<br>Design to provide acceptable safeguards for all remaining identified hazards | Outline temporary support. | Allow for use of hydraulic platform for jointing at height. |

## Examples of risk mitigation (issues addressed at different stages)

Because the top three storeys of a building cantilever out over other structures, the engineer has arranged that they structurally "hang" from a central core in the final condition. During erection, however, the steel frame can be sufficiently light as to be temporarily supported from the outrigger areas of the floors below.

| Concept design | Scheme design | Detail design |
|---|---|---|
| Establish work platform/crash deck areas and deal with tower crane oversailing to ensure practicality | Identify construction sequence to allow structure to develop on a floor-by-floor basis. | Design "hangers" also for temporary role as columns, to ensure stability at all stages of erection. |

A steel footbridge is to be erected over a busy highway which serves a housing estate, a school and a shopping precinct.

| Concept design | Scheme design | Detail design |
|---|---|---|
| A single span is chosen, to minimise working adjacent to traffic and to reduce dangers to road vehicles. | A lightweight design is adopted so that it can be lifted into place during a single weekend night-time road closure. Minimum temporary works required for temporary stability. | Connections and lifting points in the steelwork are designed to allow rapid pre-assembly adjacent to the site. |

A — GENERAL PLANNING
B — EXCAVATIONS AND FOUNDATIONS
C6 — PRIMARY STRUCTURE
D — BUILDING ELEMENTS AND BUILDING SERVICES
E — CIVIL ENGINEERING

## Related issues

References within this document

| References | Related issues |
|---|---|
| A1 | Surrounding environment will need to be considered when examining access to site. |
| A2 | Site clearance and simple demolition may be relevant for steel erection. |
| A3 | Site investigation may have to be carried out before design of the column bases. |
| A4 | Access on the site will need to be determined to ensure safe construction . |
| A5 | Site layout may affect the decisions to use steelwork. |
| C1 | General concrete. |
| C5 | General steelwork. |
| D3 | Atria – Invariably have temporary and final stability issues to be resolved. |
| D5 | Surface coatings and finishes – will always be part of erecting steelwork. |
| D10 | Vertical transportation – often a part of the stability core of a structure. |
| E4 | Bridge construction may well be constructed using steel. |
| E5 | Bridge maintenance will probably require periodic attention to steelwork details. |
| E6 | Working over/near water will be likely to use steelwork. |
| E7 | Cofferdams in water may use steel. |

## References for further guidance

Primary general references and background information given in Section 4

### Primary

- BS 5531:1988 Code of practice for safety in erecting structural frames
- HSE GS28 Parts 1 to 4 Safe erection of structures
- CIRIA C703 (2003) Crane stability on site.
- CIRIA C654 (2006) Tower crane stability
- BSCA 39/05 Guide to steel erection in windy conditions
- British Constructional Steelwork Association (There are a lot of guides on the BCSA website – see www.steelconstruction.org)

### Secondary

- Steel Construction Institute (2003) Steel Designers' Manual (Blackwell)
- CIRIA SP57 (1988) Handling of materials on site

### Background

- BS 7121: Code of Practice for safe use of cranes [several parts]

### Classification

**CAWS** Group G, **CEWS** Class M, **CI/SfB**, Code (28)h2

Read the Introduction before using the following guidelines

## Scope

- Brickwork.
- Blockwork.
- Stonework.
- Pre-assembled composite masonry/brickwork units.
- Jointing materials.
- Positioning of pre-assembled elements including setting out, locating and securing.
- Bearings/supports of pre-assembled elements.
- Temporary loading and supporting.
- Reinforcement in masonry work.

## Exclusions

- Masonry cladding (see D1).
- Gabions/crib block walls.
- Post-tensioned masonry.

## Major hazards

Refer to the Introduction for details of accident types and health risks

**Handling**
Weight, shape, transportation of units. Working space, hoists, manual handling at height.

**Hazardous substances**
Cement handling, lime and mortar mixing, chemical grouts, additives, dust.

**Access**
Delivery/offloading. Plant on site. Obstruction by other building elements. Working space restrictions.

**Crushing**
Placement of units, insufficient space for storage/working, falling objects, vehicle movements.

**Collapse**
Unpropped construction, elements being overloaded, movement joints, storage/stacking irregular units, horizontal chases, DPC debonding.

**Abrasion/cuts**
Masonry texture, wall ties, metal lathing, sheet metal
Insulation (glass fibre).

Sidebar tabs:
A — GENERAL PLANNING
B — EXCAVATIONS AND FOUNDATIONS
C7 — PRIMARY STRUCTURE
D — BUILDING ELEMENTS AND BUILDING SERVICES
E — CIVIL ENGINEERING

A — GENERAL PLANNING

B — EXCAVATIONS AND FOUNDATIONS

C7 — PRIMARY STRUCTURE

D — BUILDING ELEMENTS AND BUILDING SERVICES

E/I — CIVIL ENGINEERING

## Specific hazard identification

**Possible key considerations:**

- **Handling** – How will the units be handled? Manually or by crane?
- **Access** – What provisions are required to ensure adequate space for plant and scaffolding?
- **Temporary conditions** – What design considerations are involved?
- **Installation** – How can this be arranged to ensure healthy and safe procedures?
- **Special considerations** – What are the required procedures (eg cutting)?
- **Jointing materials** – What are these to be? How will they be applied?
- **Masonry ties** – What can be specified to make installation safer?
- **Any others?**

## Prompts

- Source of materials
- Handling units
- Handling points
- Lifting procedures
- Transporting units
- Positioning
- Temporary support
- Lime and other chemicals
- Cleaning
- Demolition

## Hazards consideration in design

| Stage | Considerations and issues | Possible design options to avoid or mitigate hazards identified for masonry |
|---|---|---|
| Concept design | • Why use masonry?<br>• Location<br>• Scope of work<br>• Familiar work<br>• Access<br>• Interfaces<br>• Sequences<br>• Materials | • The alternatives to using masonry will generally involve in-situ or pre-cast concrete. If not, design masonry that has familiar details.<br>• Can stone work be factory prepared? In particular, can site cutting of sandstone be avoided?<br>• Plan the timescale and sequence of masonry working to avoid working during bad weather, during winter months or on a congested site.<br>• Study alternative routes for access. Allow adequate working space for operatives and materials. |
| Scheme design | • Unit types<br>• Joints<br>• Handling<br>• Reinforcement<br>• Protection<br>• Tolerances<br>• Procedures<br>• Working space | • Specify materials that are least likely to create dust (eg use preformed materials).<br>• Avoid blocks above 20kg weight.<br>• Consider components that are preformed and joined on site.<br>• Consider methods of quick and secure erection.<br>• Joint design tolerances should be relevant to nature of work.<br>• Design provision for delivery and handling of materials on congested sites, close to work station if possible. |
| Detail design | • Handling<br>• Inserts/fixings<br>• Connections/joints<br>• Finishes<br>• Bearings<br>• Positioning<br>• Temporary supports | • Wherever possible use materials that are non-corrosive and non-abrasive.<br>• Specify appropriate tolerances to avoid cutting, etc. on site.<br>• If mechanical handling is necessary, incorporate lifting and handling attachment points into the design.<br>• Design-in provision for service runs, to avoid cutting on site. |

## Examples of risk mitigation (methods of solution)

| ISSUE / ACTION | Handling large blocks | Use of brickwork ties |
|---|---|---|
| **Avoidance**<br>Design to avoid identified hazards but beware of introducing others | Use blocks less than 20kg, to allow manual handling. | Specify ties without sharp edges. |
| **Reduction**<br>Design to reduce identified hazards but beware of increasing others | Detail lifting points for block handling. | Construct second skin as soon as possible. |
| **Control**<br>Design to provide acceptable safeguards for all remaining identified hazards | Specify mechanical handling for laying large blocks. | Specify temporary covers to sharp ties (if used). |

## Examples of risk mitigation (issues addressed at different stages)

A refurbishment project requires selected stonework to be removed and replaced at height from a building due to weathering and moisture ingress. The new stonework is to match the existing.

| Concept design | Scheme design | Detail design |
|---|---|---|
| Consider alternative safe methods for how the suspect stonework could be removed and replaced. | Develop a safe method of removal and replacement using scaffolding as access and also means of handling stonework. | To avoid hazards of cutting on site, special replacement stonework will be surveyed and prepared off-site. |

Internal fair-faced walls to an exhibition centre are 8 metres high and are required to have the special effect of textured large concrete blocks with decorative joints.

| Concept design | Scheme design | Detail design |
|---|---|---|
| Design for 2 leafs of blockwork, using 20kg blocks to reduce weight for manual handling. | Design 20kg blocks to incorporate provisions for the decorative joints. | Blockwork lifts not to exceed 1.5m high each day. Wall-ties selected to avoid hazards of handling and being cut by sharp edges. Highlight that care is required when using retarders. |

**GENERAL PLANNING** A

**EXCAVATIONS AND FOUNDATIONS** B

**PRIMARY STRUCTURE** C7

**BUILDING ELEMENTS AND BUILDING SERVICES** D

**CIVIL ENGINEERING** E

# C7    Group C – Primary structure
## 7 – Masonry

## Related issues

References within this document

| References | Related issues |
|---|---|
| A2 | Site clearance and simple demolition will involve the safe storage and removal of brickwork and general masonry. |
| A4 | Access onto site will need to accommodate the frequent deliveries of materials for masonry work. |
| A5 | Site layout will need to consider the safe storage of materials delivered to site for masonry work. |
| B1-B3 | Excavations are frequently for masonry work within deep excavations. Alternative methods should be considered (eg use of pre-cast rings). |
| B7 | Underpinning to foundations could involve masonry work. |
| C1-C4 | Concrete works usually interface with masonry works, with different trades working closely. |
| D1 | External cladding often incorporates masonry panels. |
| E1 | Civil Engineering small works may involve the use of engineering brickwork/masonry work, in difficult and remote locations. |

## References for further guidance

Primary general references and background information given in Section 4

### Primary

- BRE Good Building Guide 1 Repairing and replacing lintels
- HSE CIS36 Silica
- HSE CIS37 Handling building blocks
- CIRIA R117 (1988) Replacement ties in cavity walls: a guide to tie spacing and selection
- CIRIA SP57 (1988) Handling of materials on site
- CIRIA C579 (2003) Retention of masonry facades – best practice guide
- CIRIA C589 (2003) Retention of masonry facades – best practice site handbook
- CIRIA R111 (2005) Structural renovation of traditional buildings
- CIRIA C656 (2006) Masonry arch bridges: condition appraisal and remedial treatment

### Secondary

- BRE Good Building Guide 14 Building simple plan brick or blockwork freestanding walls
- BRE Defect Action Sheet 115 External masonry cavity wall, wall ties, selection and specification

### Background

- Curtin, W G et al (2006) Structural masonry designers' manual (Blackwell)
- Orton, A (1992) Structural design of masonry (Longman)
- BS 5628: Code of practice for use of masonry [several parts]
- Institution of Structural Engineers Appraisal of exiting structures (under revision)

### Classification

**CAWS** Group F,    **CEWS** Class U,    **CI/SfB** Code (2-)F

Read the Introduction before using the following guidelines

## Scope

- Softwoods.
- Hardwoods.
- Wood-based products (eg plywood, chipboard).
- Glued laminated timber (Glulam).
- Building frames.
- Roof trusses (including "gang nail" trusses).
- Trussed partitions.
- Suspended floors.
- Preservative treatments.

## Exclusions

- Repair of decayed timber.
- Fire protection of timber (cladding).
- Temporary works (falsework, shuttering, etc.).
- Support to suspect buildings.
- Surface painting.

## Major hazards

Refer to the Introduction for details of accident types and health risks

**Falls from height**
Erection sequences during installation, edge protection, platforms, access.

**Collapse**
Temporary stability. Inadequate staging/support.
Ground support for cranes.
Stacked materials.

**Health hazards**
Wood preservatives.
Adhesives, resins.
Treated timber.
Wood dust.

**Access**
Site layout, delivery routes
Storage, cranage, erection sequences.

**Mobile plant**
Delivery lorries, site transport, cranes, dumpers, inadequate working space, erection sequences.

**Handling**
Off-loading, stacking and erecting components (manual and use of crane).
Metal connectors/cleafs.
Cuts and splinters.

Right margin tabs:
- A GENERAL PLANNING
- B EXCAVATIONS AND FOUNDATIONS
- C 8 PRIMARY STRUCTURE
- D BUILDING ELEMENTS AND BUILDING SERVICES
- E CIVIL ENGINEERING

## Specific hazard identification

**Possible key considerations:**

- **Assumptions** – What are the design assumptions? Do they imply health or safety hazards?
- **Handling and storage** – How will the components be off-loaded and stored?
- **Sequences** – What are the construction sequences?
- **Access** – How will adequate access and working space be maintained?
- **Weather** – What are the likely weather conditions?
- **Installation** – What procedures are necessary for unit installation?
- **Temporary support** – What provisions will be necessary?
- **Fire walls** – What is construction against fire walls?
- **Preservatives** – What chemicals will be applied?
- **Any others?**

## Prompts

- Temporary conditions
- Transport
- Access
- Lifting points
- Positioning, alignment
- Connections
- Tolerances
- Preservatives
- Adhesives
- Demolition

## Hazards consideration in design

| Stage | Considerations and issues | Possible design options to avoid or mitigate hazards identified for timber |
|---|---|---|
| Concept design | • Why use timber?<br>• Scope of work<br>• Interfaces<br>• Site environment<br>• Programme<br>• Outline sequences<br>• Major equipment | • The alternatives to timber will usually include steel or concrete.<br>• Fire prevention is a major consideration when using timber.<br>• Study the options for access and working space, in conjunction with construction sequences available within the constraints of the site.<br>• Examine the feasibility of just-in-time delivery of pre-fabricated units. |
| Scheme design | • Access<br>• Component sizes and weights<br>• Working space<br>• Storage areas<br>• Handling methods<br>• Installation<br>• Pre-assembly<br>• Cranage | • Review component sizes and weights together with handling methods.<br>• Develop arrangements for just-in-time delivery, to enable direct placement of the unit into the final position.<br>• Identify handling methods to suit methods of supply and storage.<br>• Examine sequences of construction, to avoid unnecessary overlapping of activities and other trades. |
| Detail design | • Temporary supports<br>• Preservatives<br>• Tolerances<br>• Connections<br>• Lifting points<br>• Positioning | • If mechanical handling is necessary, incorporate lifting and handling measures into the design.<br>• Devise permanent works to incorporate temporary support.<br>• Develop joint arrangements which minimise cutting on site.<br>• Specify preservatives that are not hazardous to operatives during application; preferably apply preservatives in factory conditions. |

## Examples of risk mitigation (methods of solution)

| ISSUE | Roof erection |
|---|---|
| **ACTION** | |
| **Avoidance**<br>Design to avoid identified hazards but beware of introducing others | Design for pre-fabricated roof at ground level, place by crane. |
| **Reduction**<br>Design to reduce identified hazards but beware of increasing others | Lift trusses by crane and provide space for use of hydraulic platforms. |
| **Control**<br>Design to provide acceptable safeguards for all remaining identified hazards | Incorporate handling points and positive seating. |

GENERAL PLANNING — A

EXCAVATIONS AND FOUNDATIONS — B

PRIMARY STRUCTURE — C 8

BUILDING ELEMENTS AND BUILDING SERVICES — D

CIVIL ENGINEERING — E

## Examples of risk mitigation (issues addressed at different stages)

A leisure facility is to include a large enclosed space. The architect wishes to incorporate a timber finish to the main structural members. Site investigation results indicates that a lightweight structure is required to provide acceptable bearing pressures.

| Concept design | Scheme design | Detail design |
|---|---|---|
| Structural members are to be designed using glued-laminated timber columns and timber roof trusses. Use of timber means lower capacity cranes for erection. These can be used working within the building on a prepared granular base. | Specify allowable tolerances and temporary wind bracing requirements to ensure stability during erection. Lightweight tiles to be used. | Design pre-fabricated crane-handled hips and valley sets to minimise working at height. |

A timber structure is to be constructed against an existing Grade 1 Listed Building. Due to the unconformity of the building, significant site cutting and jointing is envisaged. The cut surfaces will need to be treated with preservatives.

| Concept design | Scheme design | Detail design |
|---|---|---|
| Design members to maximise pre-fabrication and minimise make-up pieces and site application of preservatives. | Specify application requirements for preservative treatment. Maximum in pre-fabrication works by vacuum pressure treatment. Design make-up pieces. | Design site connections to make application of preservatives easily accessible and minimise working at height. |

**A** GENERAL PLANNING

**B** EXCAVATIONS AND FOUNDATIONS

**C 8** PRIMARY STRUCTURE

**D** BUILDING ELEMENTS AND BUILDING SERVICES

**E I** CIVIL ENGINEERING

## Related issues

References within this document

| References | Related issues |
| --- | --- |
| A1 | Surrounding environment will need to be considered when examining access to the installation locations. |
| A2 | Site clearance and simple demolition may be relevant in providing adequate access and storage areas. |
| A3 | Site investigation will usually need to be carried out to determine criteria for the design of the timber structure. |
| A4 | Access onto site and adjacent to installation location will need to be considered to ensure safe construction. |
| A5 | Site layout may interact with decision to use timber construction. |
| D2 | Roofs are likely to be constructed using timber trusses. |
| E6 | Working over/near water may be an important consideration when working on timber construction. |

## References for further guidance

Primary general references and background information given in Section 4

### Primary

- TRADA (2001) Timber frame construction. 3rd ed
- CIRIA R111 (1994) Structural renovation of traditional buildings
- CIRIA SP57 (1988) Handling of materials on site
- TRADA (2005) Wood preservation – chemicals and processes

### Secondary

- Ozelton, E C and Baird, J A (2002) Timber Designer's Manual. 3rd ed (Blackwell)
- TRADA (2006) Timber frame housing: UK structural recommendations
- Gang-Nail Systems (1989) The trussed rafter manual (Gang-Nail Systems)
- BS 5268: Part 5:1989 Code of practice for preservative treatment of structural timber

### Background

- BS 5268 Structural use of timber [several parts]

### Classification

**CAWS** Group G, **CEWS** Class O, **CI/SfB** Code (2-)i

# Group D – Building elements and building services
## 1 – External cladding

Read the Introduction before using the following guidelines

## Scope

- Factory fabricated panel cladding systems.
- Site assembled traditional frame systems.
- Panel rainscreen cladding systems.
- Panel overcladding systems.
- Thin stone and brick veneers.
- Profiled metal sheeting including composite panels.

## Exclusions

- Brickwork/blockwork (see C7).
- Insulated and non-insulated renders.
- Special glass assemblies (eg Pilkington's Planar Glazing)
- Special finishes (eg patination).
- Restoration.

## Major hazards

Refer to the Introduction for details of accident types and health risks

**Working at height**
Workers falling during erection, cleaning, maintenance and repair. Dropped objects during erection, maintenance and repair.

**Replacement**
Access, size of pieces to be moved round building and into position, ease of removal, safe fixing.

**Glazing**
Accidental breakage, site glazing, replacement glazing from outside, large pieces of glass, annealed glass.

**Handling/transportation**
Many stages - on/off lorries, in/out of storage, up/down building, into final position on building, repair/maintenance.

**Hazardous operations**
Surveys prior to installation. Glazing, testing, site welding, cutting, maintenance.

**Hazardous substance**
Paints, sealants, insulating materials.

GENERAL PLANNING **A**

EXCAVATIONS AND FOUNDATIONS **B**

PRIMARY STRUCTURE **C**

BUILDING ELEMENTS AND BUILDING SERVICES **D** **1**

CIVIL ENGINEERING **E**

# D1 Group D – Building elements and building services
## 1 – External cladding

**A** — GENERAL PLANNING

**B** — EXCAVATIONS AND FOUNDATIONS

**C** — PRIMARY STRUCTURE

**D 1** — BUILDING ELEMENTS AND BUILDING SERVICES

**E** — CIVIL ENGINEERING

## Specific hazard identification

**Possible key considerations:**

- **Building location** - Are there particular access problems? Do the public have to be protected? Will the site exclude using particular plant, cladding system or materials?

    **Building form** - Can the cladding be prefabricated? Can large panels be installed and fixed safely to all elevations? Are there any difficult to construct features (eg overhangs)?

- **Repair and maintenance** - What suitable methods and equipment for cleaning, inspection and maintenance? Will this equipment allow replacement of pieces of cladding (eg glass)?

- **Life of cladding** - Will some or all elements of the cladding need replacement? Can replacement be carried out safely? Can the cladding be dismantled safely?

## Prompts

- Materials (heavy/light)
- Size of pieces (man lift or machine)
- Life to first maintenance and failure maintenance
- Glaze from inside or out
- Replacement
- Fixings (easy to install)
- Access to site
- Access round the building
- Adjustment/alignment/tolerances
- Any restricted spaces
- Jointing/sealing
- Cleaning
- Large and lightweight panels
- Wind loading effect

## Hazards consideration in design

| Stage | Considerations and issues | Possible design options to avoid or mitigate hazards identified for external cladding |
|---|---|---|
| Concept design | • Location<br>• Building shape<br>• Form of construction | • Study forms of cladding construction that allow safe working space for operatives and safe lining and levelling once on the building.<br>• Check whether planning/budgetary/client restraints permit the use of permanently installed facade cleaning and maintenance equipment.<br>• Identify variations to the building shape which suit cladding that can be constructed, cleaned and maintained safely. |
| Scheme design | • Access for plant/people<br>• Cleaning, repair and maintenance<br>• Sequence of operations<br>• Method of assembly<br>• Element size/weight<br>• Interfaces<br>• Temporary conditions<br>• Connections/fixings<br>• Adjustment/alignment<br>• Testing | • Develop cladding details to provide primary attachments that are safe and easy to use in all locations.<br>• Develop cladding jointing details that permit safe and easy installation.<br>• Design elements so that they can be cleaned and replaced safely. |
| Detail design | | • If mechanical handling is required, incorporate lifting and handling measures into the design.<br>• If restraints are required for cleaning and maintenance equipment incorporate these into the design.<br>• Co-ordinate with designer of structural frame to ensure primary fixings are safe and easy to install. |

## Examples of risk mitigation (methods of solution)

| ACTION / ISSUE | Falls during cleaning | Hazardous operation fixings |
|---|---|---|
| **Avoidance**<br>Design to avoid identified hazards but beware of introducing others | Provide permanently installed access equipment that can be entered without stepping over a building edge. | Provide primary attachments to the frame that slot together without the need for loose bolts. |
| **Reduction**<br>Design to reduce identified hazards but beware of increasing others | Provide suitable access round the building to allow lorry-mounted access platforms to reach all parts of the facade. | Provide primary attachments to the frame that allow bolts to be placed without the need to work overhead. |
| **Control**<br>Design to provide acceptable safeguards for all remaining identified hazards | Provide a comprehensive system of attachments and latchway wires for personal protective equipment. | Provide a greater number of primary attachments to the frame so that smaller bolts can be used. |

## Examples of risk mitigation (issues addressed at different stages)

An existing office building in the centre of a major city is to be refurbished and reclad. The building is bounded on two sides by existing buildings and on the other two sides by very busy city streets and public pavements. There is no room for a crane or a large hoist, and the internal goods lift is small.

| Concept design | Scheme design | Detail design |
|---|---|---|
| Large prefabricated panels cannot be lifted. A traditional aluminium framing system is appropriate with infill elements designed to fit the lifting arrangements and access round the building. | The sequence of operations is planned so that the elements needed to complete sections of wall are delivered to site in crates of a size to suit the lifting arrangements and access round the building. | Design the primary attachments so that they can be safely installed from the inside at each floor level. |

The project involves the overcladding of a seven-storey block of local authority flats. The block is brick-clad, concrete framed, with timber-framed single-glazed windows. The local authority wants to change the municipal appearance, improve thermal performance and reduce maintenance costs without moving the occupants.

| Concept design | Scheme design | Detail design |
|---|---|---|
| A metal rainscreen overcladding system with insulation behind meets the brief. The issues associated with fixing insulation and the problems of noise/dust/isolation when installing fixings need to be considered. | A cleaning and maintenance strategy is developed to allow windows to be cleaned from inside and the main facade from roof mounted access equipment. | A sequence of operation is developed for removing existing windows and filling new ones into the overcladding system without too much disruptions to the occupiers. |

Sidebar tabs:
- A — GENERAL PLANNING
- B — EXCAVATIONS AND FOUNDATIONS
- C — PRIMARY STRUCTURE
- D / 1 — BUILDING ELEMENTS AND BUILDING SERVICES
- E — CIVIL ENGINEERING

## Related issues

References within this document

| References | Related issues |
|------------|----------------|
| D6 | Cleaning and maintenance is fundamental to cladding design and must be considered at the earliest possible time. |
| A4 | Access onto and around the site may dictate the cladding that has to be used. |
| C1-C8 | Primary structure will dictate the type of fixing and the amount of adjustment required to take up tolerances safely. |
| | Interfaces for different trades will dictate sequencing of operations and replacement and maintenance strategies. |
| | Operators should be aware that maintenance and repair companies are sometimes less knowledgeable than the original installers/designers. Keep maintenance and repair to a minimum by good design and the use of appropriate materials. |
| | Occupied buildings, maintain safe access/egress and fire escape if the building is occupied while work is in progress. |

## References for further guidance

Primary general references and background information given in Section 4

### Primary

- CIRIA 632 (2005) Guidance for glazing at height
- CIRIA SP57 (1988) Handling of materials on site
- Glass and Glazing Federation (2005) Glazing manual
- BS 6262 Glazing for buildings [several parts]
- BS 8213:2004 Windows doors and rooflights. Design for safety in use and during cleaning of windows, including door-height windows and roof windows. Code of practice
- Advisory Committee for Roofwork (ACR) – www.roofworkadvice.info, various guides

### Secondary

- Centre for Window and Cladding Technology: various publications
- HSE CIS5 (revised) Temporarily suspended access cradles and platforms
- CIRIA B5 (1988) Rainscreen cladding, a guide to design principles and practice
- CIRIA C524 (2000) Cladding fixings

### Background

- BS 6206:1981 Specification for impact performance requirements for flat safety glass and safety plastics for use in buildings
- BS 6037-1:2003 Code of practice for the planning, design and installation and use of permanently installed access equipment. Suspended access equipment
- BS 5974:1990 Code of practice for temporarily installed suspended scaffolds and access equipment
- HSE PM30 Suspended access equipment

### Classification

**CAWS** Group H,    **CEWS** Class Z,    **CI/SfB** Code (41)

Sidebar tabs:

A — GENERAL PLANNING

B — EXCAVATIONS AND FOUNDATIONS

C — PRIMARY STRUCTURE

D1 — BUILDING ELEMENTS AND BUILDING SERVICES

E — CIVIL ENGINEERING

Read the Introduction before using the following guidelines

## Scope

- Flat roofs.
- Pitched roofs.
- Terraces and balconies.
- Car park/service decks.
- Skylights and rooflights.

## Exclusions

- Fabric and membrane roofs (tents).
- Temporary protection roofs.
- Mansard roofs.
- Prefabricated domes, etc.

## Major hazards

Refer to the Introduction for details of accident types and health risks

**Falls from heights**
Working at heights on steep pitches and slippery surfaces. Fragile roofs/rooflights. Lack of edge protection.

**Access**
Maintenance of roof and plant. Permanent or occasional use by building occupants, contractor (eg fire escape).

**Hazardous materials and Hazardous operations:**
Hot asphalt and bitumen, solvents and volatiles. Welding and soldering of metalwork.

**Collapse**
Temporary support structure, construction platform and permanent works.

**Handling**
Transport and handling of materials to and across the roof. Hazards from weight, size, temperature or chemical nature of materials.

**Falling or dropping**
Onto people below roof level. Items falling from unprotected roof perimeter or fragile zones within roof area (eg rooflights).

## Group D – Building elements and building services
## 2 – Roof coverings and finishes

**D2**

A — GENERAL PLANNING

B — EXCAVATIONS AND FOUNDATIONS

C — PRIMARY STRUCTURE

D2 — BUILDING ELEMENTS AND BUILDING SERVICES

E — CIVIL ENGINEERING

### Specific hazard identification

**Possible key considerations:**

- What are the benefits of pitched versus flat roofs?
- What provisions and assumptions are made for temporary stability and safety?
- What provision is made for the effects of wind during construction and maintenance?
- Is the roof construction designed to minimise risks from exposure to chemicals (solvents/fumes) and hot materials?
- What are the weather conditions likely to be during installation?
- What are the fire risks?
- What people access is proposed for roof maintenance?
- Are there general or localised weak zones in the accessible roof area (eg. rooflights)?
- Can permanent edge protection/protected walkways be incorporated?
- Size and weight vs handling and wind resistance.

### Prompts

- Stability and support
- Access
- Transport of materials
- Solvents and volatiles
- Hot working
- Rainwater disposal
- Windspeed and exposure
- Falling/dropping
- Design life
- Maintenance
- Edge protection
- Panel/roll size
- Fragility of materials
- Flashings (lead vs EPDM)

### Hazards consideration in design

| Stage | Considerations and issues | Possible design options to avoid or mitigate hazards identified for roof coverings and finishes |
|---|---|---|
| Concept design | | • A flat roof can provide a more secure work platform and access for maintenance.<br>• A pitched roof can have a longer design life and require less maintenance. |
| Scheme design | • Flat versus pitched<br>• Building structure influence on roof type and covering.<br>• Wind/rain exposure<br>• Sequence of construction activities<br>• Access to site and roof<br>• Stability and support<br>• Selection of roof system<br>• Maintenance access<br>• Lead flashing | • Security of roof components during construction and service will be affected by wind speed.<br>• Particular wind phenomena occur at near roof perimeters and ridge.<br>• The sequencing of roof construction will influence the risks of falling, temporary instability, weather hazards and problems of temporary storage on the roof.<br>• Consideration needs to be given to the stability and support of each stage - temporary or permanent - of the roof construction; allow for possible loads at both stages. |
| Detail design | | • Selection of materials, handling and fixing to minimise hazards from installation.<br>• When the design options will determine a sequence of working, favour the option/sequence which minimises the risks from temporary instability, lack of support, inclement weather working, difficult local access - partial covering of work by other traders. |

## Examples of risk mitigation (methods of solution)

| ISSUE<br><br>ACTION | Flat roof membrane | Translucent fragile panels |
|---|---|---|
| **Avoidance**<br>Design to avoid identified hazards but beware of introducing others | Loose lay cold membranes to avoid the use of hot bitumen. | Use alternative stronger material. |
| **Reduction**<br>Design to reduce identified hazards but beware of increasing others | Use torch-applied bonding or solvents/adhesives to secure pre-formed products. | Use a thicker material or additional layers of material. |
| **Control**<br>Design to provide acceptable safeguards for all remaining identified hazards | Specify safety provisions. | Provide a walkway/grille over the fragile panels. |

## Examples of risk mitigation (issues addressed at different stages)

A large factory requires fast construction to bring the facility on stream. It is preferred that the roof be finished early in the programme so that other construction and fitting out can take place beneath in protected conditions.

| Concept design | Scheme design | Detail design |
|---|---|---|
| Cost, programme considerations and repetitive nature of construction lead to choice of flat roof which can quickly follow frame erection. Rapid placement of metal decking not only provides safer work platform for use at height but also protects remainder of workforce at ground level from dropped objects and inclement weather. | Roofing materials to be mechanically fixed to minimise time spent at height and complexity/hazards of these work activities. | Final detailing of gutters/eaves to incorporate provision for edge protection primarily for construction, but which can also be exploited during maintenance. |

Design of a pitched roofed warehouse with valley gutters.
The "traditional" roof appearance is preferred because of existing architecture and technical concerns.

| Concept design | Scheme design | Detail design |
|---|---|---|
| Consider choice of roofing sheets. Reject fragile material as roof access is required for cleaning gutters. | Appropriate non-fragile material selected. | Make valley gutter wide and strong enough to walk along. Provide permanent edge protection at gable ends of gutters. |

**A** GENERAL PLANNING

**B** EXCAVATIONS AND FOUNDATIONS

**C** PRIMARY STRUCTURE

**D2** BUILDING ELEMENTS AND BUILDING SERVICES

**E** CIVIL ENGINEERING

## Related issues

References within this document

| References | Related issues |
|---|---|
| A1 | Surrounding environment will need to be assessed for access routes for materials and prevailing wind conditions. |
| A4 | Access onto and within the site will need to be considered. |
| A5 | Site layout could be influenced by roof construction type and associated methods. |
| C1-C8 | Primary structure can influence roof construction options. |
| C8 | Timber will often be used for trusses supporting roof coverings. |
| D1 | External cladding details and roofs interact. |
| D4 | Windows/glazing may be included in roofs and will require cleaning. |
| D7 | Mechanical plant for services often have to be roof-mounted. |
| D8 | Lightning protection. |

## References for further guidance

Primary general references and background information given in Section 4

### Primary

- HSG33 Health and safety in roofwork (under revision)
- CITB – Construction site safety, Vol 1, Section C6, Safe working on roofs and at heights (2003)
- BEC Construction Safety, Section 15 Work on roofs
- HSE INDG 284 Working on roofs
- BRE Designing safe roofs –Digest 493
- Advisory Committee for Roofwork (ACR) – www.roofworkadvice.info, various guides

### Secondary

- BS 6229: 2003 Flat roofs with continuously supported coverings
- BS 5534: 2003 Code of practice for slating and tiling
- BS 6915: 2001 Design and construction of fully supported lead sheet roof and wall coverings
- HSE CIS5 (revised) Temporarily suspended access cradles and platforms
- HSE L132 Approved code of practice and guidance – Control of lead at work regulations 2002
- CIRIA 632 (2005) Guidance for glazing at height

### Background

- Copper Development Association (1992) Copper in Roofing Pocket Book
- CIRIA and BFRC B15 (1993) Flat Roofing guide: Design and good practice
- BRE Report 302 (1996) Roofs and roofing: performance, diagnosis, maintenance, repair and the avoidance of defects (BRE)
- Mindham, C N (2006) Roof construction and loft conversion. 4th ed (Blackwell)

### Classification

**CAWS** Group H, **CEWS** Class W, **CI/SfB** Code (47)

Read the Introduction before using the following guidelines

## Scope

- Walls to atria.
- Roofs to atria.
- Roofs to shopping malls.

## Exclusions

- Internal partitions.
- Rooflights and skylights.

## Major hazards

Refer to the Introduction for details of accident types and health risks

**Working at height**
Falling from height, cleaning, maintenance and repair, access.
Dropped objects.

**Hazardous materials**
Paints, sealants, glass.

**Handling**
Many stages on/off lorries, in/out of storage, up/down building into final position on building, repair maintenance.

**Glazing**
Site glazing, glazing from outside, large pieces of glass, replacement, accidental breakage, metal/glass contact.

**Hazardous operations**
Inspections, glazing and reglazing, cleaning and maintenance, servicing smoke vents.

Side tabs:
A — GENERAL PLANNING
B — EXCAVATIONS AND FOUNDATIONS
C — PRIMARY STRUCTURE
D 3 — BUILDING ELEMENTS AND BUILDING SERVICES
E — CIVIL ENGINEERING

**A** GENERAL PLANNING

**B** EXCAVATIONS AND FOUNDATIONS

**C** PRIMARY STRUCTURE

**D3** BUILDING ELEMENTS AND BUILDING SERVICES

**E** CIVIL ENGINEERING

## Specific hazard identification

**Possible key considerations:**

- **Installation** - Has access for installation been considered? Do the public have to be protected? Will scaffolding be required? How are elements to be lifted? Fixed?

- **Cleaning and maintenance** - Consideration to be given to cleaning inside and outside. How is access for cleaning and maintenance to be achieved? Consider how replacement is carried out. Will other services interfere with cleaning?

- **Injury from falling objects** - Consider the use of safe materials overhead (eg laminated glass)? Can features be designed to protect people below from falling objects? Consider the use of handrails and other barriers to stop people and objects striking glass.

## Prompts

- Access
- Maintenance
- Replacement
- People overhead
- Handling
- Occupied premises
- Tolerances
- Fixings (easy to reach)
- Jointing and sealing
- Other services
- Confined spaces

## Hazards consideration in design

| Stage | Considerations and issues | Possible design options to avoid or mitigate hazards identified for atria |
|---|---|---|
| Concept design | • Access<br>• Cleaning and maintenance<br>• Form of construction<br>• Shape and size<br>• Design life<br>• Element size/weight | • Consider using purpose-designed permanently installed access equipment inside and outside overhead glazing for cleaning, maintenance and glass replacement.<br>• Ensure safe access can be provided for installation<br>• Ensure access to cleaning and maintenance equipment provided can be achieved safely. |
| Scheme design | • Sequence<br>• Cranage<br>• Repair replacement<br>• Types of glass and configuration<br>• Connections/fixings<br>• Assembly<br>• Temporary conditions during erection | • The design of the glazing system and associated cleaning equipment should maximise factory prefabrication.<br>• Any external temporary scaffolding roofs required for construction should be designed to allow smoke extraction in the event of a fire. |
| Detail design | • Adjustment/<br>• Alignment<br>• Surveys of supporting structure<br>• Testing of cleaning equipment<br>• Sequence of assembly | • Fixing details for overhead glazing need to be detailed so that they can be secured without working overhead and blind.<br>• Glazing systems need to be designed so that glass can be replaced without danger of whole sheets falling onto operatives. |

## Examples of risk mitigation (methods of solution)

| ACTION \ ISSUE | Falls during maintenance | Injury from falling objects |
|---|---|---|
| **Avoidance** Design to avoid identified hazards but beware of introducing others | Provide permanently-installed access equipment inside and outside the roofs to atria that can be entered without stepping over a building edge or onto the roof. | Use materials that will not fall out of supporting framework if they are broken accidentally. |
| **Reduction** Design to reduce identified hazards but beware of increasing others | Consider a strategy for maintenance that involves the regular erection of purpose designed scaffolding with access platforms at appropriate levels to allow safe working methods to be used. | Provide features below that will catch falling objects and direct them to areas where they will do no harm. |
| **Control** Design to provide acceptable safeguards for all remaining identified hazards | Provide a comprehensive system of attachments and latchway wires for personal protective equipment, with safe access onto these systems. | Prevent or limit access to the vulnerable elements by barriers or protection. |

## Examples of risk mitigation (issues addressed at different stages)

A glass roof over an atrium has suffered from spontaneous fracture of toughened glass panes due to nickel sulphide inclusions. The owner wishes to re-glaze the roof while the building is still in use. The base of the atrium is 5 storeys below the roof and is used as a circulation area.

| Concept design | Scheme design | Detail design |
|---|---|---|
| A scaffolding will be erected with a working deck just below the roof. Temporary roofing will go over the glass roof. | Consider options for supporting the working deck/crash deck and temporary smoke control. | Identify risks associated with the assumed sequence and method of dismantling. |

A new shopping centre is to be constructed. The mall between the shops is to have a glazed roof.

| Concept design | Scheme design | Detail design |
|---|---|---|
| Consider various forms for the glazed roof that will allow for cleaning and maintenance. Assess options for access to building and maintenance equipment | Consider various types of cleaning equipment that can be used and select the one that offers the easiest and safest access for installation and maintenance. | Design safe and unobstructed access for maintenance cleaning equipment. |

Side tab index:
- GENERAL PLANNING — A
- EXCAVATIONS AND FOUNDATIONS — B
- PRIMARY STRUCTURE — C
- BUILDING ELEMENTS AND BUILDING SERVICES — D 3
- CIVIL ENGINEERING — E

## D3

# Group D – Building elements and building services
# 3 – Atria

## Related issues

References within this document

| References | Related issues |
| --- | --- |
| A4 | Access onto the site and access for installing and cleaning atria cladding will dictate the form of cladding to be used and the sequence and method of assembly. |
| C1-C8 | Primary structure will dictate the types and method of fixing and the amount of adjustment required to take up tolerances. |
| D6 | Cleaning and maintenance is fundamental to atria design and must be considered at the earliest possible time. |
| | Interfaces for different trades will dictate sequencing of operations and replacement and maintenance strategies. |
| | Operators should be aware that maintenance and repair companies are sometimes less knowledgeable than the original installers/designers. Hence minimise maintenance and repair in design and use appropriate materials. |
| | Occupied building, maintain safe access/egress and fire escape if the building is occupied while construction cleaning or maintenance work is in progress. |
| | |

## References for further guidance

Primary general references and background information given in Section 4

### Primary

- CIRIA 632 (2005) Guidance for glazing at height
- Centre for Window and Cladding Technology publications
- Glass and Glazing Federation (2005) Glazing manual
- BS 5516: 2004 Patent glazing and sloping glazing for buildings. 2 parts.
- CIRIA Publication SP87 (1992) Wall technology volumes A to G

### Secondary

- BS 6037 Code of practice for the planning, design, installation and use of permanently installed access equipment. 2 parts
- Dawson S, Cleaning System for Glass Dome. Architects Journal, Jan 98

### Background

- CIRIA SP57 (1988) Handling of materials on site
- HSE CIS5 (revised) Temporarily suspended access cradles and platforms
- HSE PM30 Suspended access equipment
- BRE Report 258 (1994) Design approaches for smoke control in atrium buildings (BRE)

### Classification

**CAWS** Group H, **CEWS** Class Z, **CI/SfB** Code (--) 913

Read the Introduction before using the following guidelines

## Scope

- New windows.
- Replacement windows.
- Windows in curtain walling.
- Windows in overcladding.
- Windows in brickwork/blockwork/stonework.
- Domestic windows.

## Exclusions

- Rooflights/skylights (see D2).
- Special loading conditions (eg bomb blast).
- Smoke ventilators.

## Major hazards

Refer to the Introduction for details of accident types and health risks

**Working at height**
Falling from height, cleaning, maintenance and repair, access, dropped objects.

**Cleaning and maintenance**
Outside of window difficult/dangerous to reach, rarely provision for access and working place.

**Replacement**
Access through occupied spaces and lack of protection outside.

**Handling transportation**
Many stages, on/off lorries, in/out of storage, up/down building, into final position on building.

**Hazardous operations**
Surveys prior to installation, glazing, testing cleaning and maintenance.

**Hazardous materials**
Paints, sealants, insulating materials, glass.

GENERAL PLANNING   A

EXCAVATIONS AND FOUNDATIONS   B

PRIMARY STRUCTURE   C

BUILDING ELEMENTS AND BUILDING SERVICES   D 4

CIVIL ENGINEERING   E

A — GENERAL PLANNING

B — EXCAVATIONS AND FOUNDATIONS

C — PRIMARY STRUCTURE

D 4 — BUILDING ELEMENTS AND BUILDING SERVICES

E — CIVIL ENGINEERING

## Specific hazard identification

**Possible key considerations:**

- **Installation** - Has access for installation been considered? Will the site exclude using particular plant or equipment? How are windows lifted? How are they fixed? Can the pieces be easily handled, moved and installed?

- **Cleaning and maintenance** - How is access for cleaning and maintenance achieved? How is replacement carried out? How will windows be opened for cleaning? Will size of opening light limit cleaning and maintenance options? Will permanently installed equipment be provided for the outside of the building.

- **Occupied buildings** - will the windows be installed, cleaned and maintained from inside the building? Will special tools or procedures be required to remove windows or glass in the event of failure? Access and escape routes need to be maintained at all times. Reduce hazardous operations to a minimum. Will other services interfere with installation, cleaning and maintenance?

## Prompts

- Space to align local access
- Low cills
- Safe reach to outside
- Replacement
- Building in use
- Low maintenance materials
- Glaze from inside
- Adjustment/alignment
- Size of glass pieces

## Hazards consideration in design

| Stage | Considerations and issues | Possible design options to avoid or mitigate hazards identified for windows |
|---|---|---|
| Concept design | • Building shape/size<br>• Location<br>• Cleaning strategy<br>• Repair/maintenance | • Consider options for cleaning maintenance and repair which include permanent or temporary access equipment.<br>• To reduce maintenance requirements consider low maintenance options like coated aluminium or UPVC rather than timber.<br>• Consider types of window to assist with cleaning and maintenance, eg centre pivot or reversible. |
| Scheme design | • Form of construction<br>• Opening type<br>• Size of opening light<br>• Temporary conditions<br>• Connections fixings<br>• Types of glass<br>• Limiting stays<br>• Opening devices<br>• Locking devices | • Replacement strategy will dictate the size of glass and window framing that can be moved through an occupied building.<br>• Design of fixing should consider ease of adjustment for building tolerances and easy access from inside for replacement. |
| Detail design | • Sequence of assembly<br>• Fixing details<br>• Glazing details | • Detail stays, restraints or guard rails to prevent window cleaners from falling out.<br>• Detail components so that each element can be fixed and weathered without blind or overhead working. |

## Examples of risk mitigation (methods of solution)

| | Falls during cleaning |
|---|---|
| **ISSUE** / **ACTION** | |
| **Avoidance** <br> Design to avoid identified hazards but beware of introducing others | Clean externally from permanently installed access equipment that can be entered without stepping over a building edge, and limit size of windows so that they can be cleaned internally standing on the floor. |
| **Reduction** <br> Design to reduce identified hazards but beware of increasing others | Provide centre pivot or reversible windows of limited size so that both sides can be cleaned safely from inside the building standing on the floor. |
| **Control** <br> Design to provide acceptable safeguards for all remaining identified hazards | Provide inward opening windows of limited size and with locking stays so that both sides can be cleaned safely from inside the building standing on the floor and provide guard rails to protect the opening while the window is open. |

## Examples of risk mitigation (issues addressed at different stages)

A high rise office block by the sea is to have new windows fitted. Complaints about the air-conditioning from the users require the new windows to provide natural ventilation. The building will remain occupied during the work, though there will be a phased decanting of floors to allow the recladding work to proceed.

| Concept design | Scheme design | Detail design |
|---|---|---|
| Consider whether reversible inward opening or pivot windows in the sizes required can be safely opened for cleaning in a windy environment. Can windows of the required size be installed from inside the building or does a strategy for installation, maintenance and replacement from outside have to be developed. | Consider the various types of the window selected and develop sequences of operations for installation and replacement that offer the easiest and safest means of access and egress. | Specify a window type that allows only narrow opening in everyday use, but wider opening with a special key for cleaning. |

An extension of an existing building requires windows to match existing Georgian sash windows, but for acoustic reasons need to be triple glazed. The stone facade will not be cleaned regularly, the windows need to be cleaned regularly.

| Concept design | Scheme design | Detail design |
|---|---|---|
| Establish a sequence of opening procedures that allows all faces of each piece of glazing to be reached from inside the building. | Confirm that the inward opening elements do not trap the cleaner or cause him to be pushed out of the window. | Detail the operating handles and safety catches to match the required sequence of opening and cleaning. |

A — GENERAL PLANNING

B — EXCAVATIONS AND FOUNDATIONS

C — PRIMARY STRUCTURE

D4 — BUILDING ELEMENTS AND BUILDING SERVICES

E — CIVIL ENGINEERING

## Related issues

References within this document

| References | Related issues |
|---|---|
| A4 | Access - Access onto the site and access for installing and cleaning windows will dictate the type of window used, and the sequence and method of installation. |
| C1-C8 | Primary structure - the structure surrounding the windows will dictate the type and method of fixing and the amount of adjustment required to take up tolerances safely. |
| D6 | Cleaning and maintenance - the strategy for cleaning and maintenance is fundamental to window design and must be considered at the earliest possible time. |
| | Interfaces - interfacing trades will dictate sequencing of operations and replacement and maintenance strategies. |
| | Operators - be aware that maintenance and repair companies are sometimes less knowledgable than the original installers/designers - so keep maintenance and repair to a minimum by good design and the use of appropriate materials. |
| | Occupied buildings - maintain safe access/egress and fire escape if the building is occupied while construction cleaning, maintenance or repair work is in progress. |

## References for further guidance

Primary general references and background information given in Section 4

### Primary

* CIRIA 632 (2005) Guidance for glazing at height
* Centre for Window and Cladding Technology publications
* Glass and Glazing Federation (2005) Glazing manual
* BS 8213-1: 2004 Windows doors and rooflights. Design for safety in use and during cleaning of windows, including door-height windows and roof windows. Code of practice
* BS 6262: Glazing for buildings [several parts]
* Building Regulations Part N (2000). N1 Glazing – Safety in relation to impact, opening and cleaning

### Secondary

* BS 2830:1994 Specification for suspended access equipment (suspended chairs, traditional steeplejack's seats, work cages, cradles and platforms) for use in the building, engineering construction, steeplejack and cleaning industries
* BS 5974:1990 Code of practice for temporarily installed suspended scaffolds and access equipment
* BS 6037 Code of practice for the planning, design, installation and use of permanently installed access equipment. 2 parts
* HSE CIS5 (revised) Temporarily suspended access cradles and platforms
* HSE PM30 Suspended access equipment.
* Building Control Journal – Cleaning Windows 1997 (Alternative ways)

### Background

* BS 6206:1981 (1994) Specification for impact performance requirements for flat safety glass and safety plastics for use in buildings
* HSE MISC 612 – Rope Access

### Classification

**CAWS** Group L, **CEWS** Class Z, **CI/SfB** Code (31.4)

Read the Introduction before using the following guidelines

## Scope

- Decorative coatings (paints) for timber, steel, concrete, plaster, masonry.
- Plaster, render and screeds.
- Corrosion and fire protection coatings (dry and wet systems).
- Floor and wall tiling.

## Exclusions

- Composite sheet or board linings and cladding.

GENERAL PLANNING — A

EXCAVATIONS AND FOUNDATIONS — B

PRIMARY STRUCTURE — C

BUILDING ELEMENTS AND BUILDING SERVICES — D 5

CIVIL ENGINEERING — E

## Major hazards

Refer to the Introduction for details of accident types and health risks

**Toxic solvents**
Solvents/volatiles from treatments or cleaning materials released into work space. Toxicity/suffocation if insufficient ventilation.

**Fire**
Combustibility and surface fire spread (including smoke).

**Access and workplatform**
Safety during application and maintenance.

**Hazardous substances**
Manmade mineral fibres, solvents, dust (silica).

**Manual handling**
Transport, storage and mixing of bulky/heavy materials.

**Health**
Noise, fume, dust. Resins and glues.

# D5 Group D – Building elements and building services
## 5 – Surface coatings and finishings

**A** — GENERAL PLANNING

**B** — EXCAVATIONS AND FOUNDATIONS

**C** — PRIMARY STRUCTURE

**D5** — BUILDING ELEMENTS AND BUILDING SERVICES

**E** — CIVIL ENGINEERING

## Specific hazard identification

**Possible key considerations:**

- **Handling and storage** - How will materials be off-loaded and stored?
- **Mixing** - What, if any, are the requirements?
- **Application method** - What are the options and implications?
- **Surface pre-treatment** - What operations are required?
- **Application** - What access to place of work is needed?
- **Weather conditions** - What are the application limitations?
- **Maintenance** - What are the requirements?
- **Materials** - What is the chemical nature?
- **Fire** - Is there a risk during application?
- **Any others?**

## Prompts

- Solvents
- Transport
- Mixing
- Dust/fumes
- Maintenance
- Application equipment
- Access/place of work
- Working at height

## Hazards consideration in design

| Stage | Considerations and issues | Possible design options to avoid or mitigate hazards identified for surface coatings and finishings |
|---|---|---|
| Concept design | • Why apply a finish?<br>• Why spray apply finish?<br>• Outline sequences<br>• Compatibility of materials<br>• Working space | • Can the same, or sufficient performance be achieved for the substrate without an applied finish (eg for light reflectance, or corrosion allowance)?<br>• To what extent does the nature of the specific material selected, and its requirements for application either reduce hazards or generate new ones?<br>• Sequence of construction consideration can identify situations where unacceptable hazards might occur (eg confined spaces and solvent release, working in unacceptable weather).<br>• Do materials or components in contact require special pretreatment which might introduce a hazard (eg chemical interaction or relative movements)? |
| Scheme design | • Working environment<br>• Ventilation<br>• Pre-treatment<br>• Handling<br>• Access<br>• Materials selection | • Is sufficient space allowed for the operations and maintenance?<br>• Is the working environment likely to be safe from hazards (eg toxic/suffocating fume release)?<br>• Can pre-treatment be avoided without loss of performance? |
| Detail design | • Working sequence<br>• Check existing surfaces | • Choose pre-blended/pre-mixed materials to reduce handling.<br>• Select solvent-less or water-based products wherever possible.<br>• Study routes for access and handling materials and components.<br>• Can materials be brought safely to the point of application?<br>• Can the working sequence be modified to allow for better access or control of working environment? |

## Examples of risk mitigation (methods of solution)

| ACTION \ ISSUE | Combustibility/fire spread | Access for application |
|---|---|---|
| **Avoidance**<br>Design to avoid identified hazards but beware of introducing others | Use non-combustible products. | Factory preparation of substrate and application of coatings and finishes to avoid site work. |
| **Reduction**<br>Design to reduce identified hazards but beware of increasing others | Use product of limited combustibility. | Only final layer/top coat or touching up to be site applied. |
| **Control**<br>Design to provide acceptable safeguards for all remaining identified hazards | Limit application to low risk areas. | Access to height to be controlled by principal contractor. |

## Examples of risk mitigation (issues addressed at different stages)

A commercial office development wishes to offer prestige accommodation at an economic price. Space within the building for "non-productive" areas is under close scrutiny.

Plant rooms are only accessible by maintenance staff.

| Concept design | Scheme design | Detail design |
|---|---|---|
| Plan space for optimum balance of plant requirements and maintenance of plant and surface finishes. | Provide access routes from outside building.<br>Design adequate space for safe access to and maintenance of items of plants in plant rooms as well as access to walls, floors, etc. for maintenance of finishes. | If walls/floor need painting, select coatings which require little surface preparation, are water-based and/or solvent free and require low maintenance. |

An existing warehouse is to be upgraded. The proposed works include fire - rating the steel frame.

| Concept design | Scheme design | Detail design |
|---|---|---|
| Consider whether "dry" materials (board linings) can be used instead of "wet" materials (intumescent paint). | Consider the space available for the works and consider a method that minimises the hazards. | If "wet", specify pre-blended/mixed materials to reduce handling on site. Select solvent-free or water-based products wherever possible.<br>If "dry", specify factory-cut boards. |

Side tabs: A GENERAL PLANNING · B EXCAVATIONS AND FOUNDATIONS · C PRIMARY STRUCTURE · D5 BUILDING ELEMENTS AND BUILDING SERVICES · E CIVIL ENGINEERING

# Group D – Building elements and building services
## 5 – Surface coatings and finishings

A GENERAL PLANNING

B EXCAVATIONS AND FOUNDATIONS

C PRIMARY STRUCTURE

D5 BUILDING ELEMENTS AND BUILDING SERVICES

E CIVIL ENGINEERING

## Related issues

References within this document

| References | Related issues |
|---|---|
| A4 | Access onto site will need to accommodate frequent deliveries of materials. |
| A5 | Site layout will need to be considered for the delivery of materials to the point of application, and the safe storage of materials. |
| C2 | In-situ concrete often has particular finishes specified. |
| C5 | Structural Steelwork is often site painted. |
| C8 | Timber treatments on site need to be planned with great care. |

## References for further guidance

Primary general references and background information given in Section 4

### Primary

- CIRIA C652 (2006) Safer surfaces to walk on – reducing the risk of slipping
- HSE CIS24 Chemical cleaners
- HSE CIS27 Solvents
- BS 8481: 2006 Design, preparation and application of internal gypsum, cement, cement and lime plastering systems
- BS EN 13914-1: 2005 Design, preparation and application of external rendering and internal plastering. External rendering
- BS 6150: 2006 Painting of buildings
- BS 8000 Part 10: 1995 Workmanship on building sites: Code of practice for plastering and rendering
- BS 8000 Part 12: 1989 Workmanship on building sites: Code of practice for decorative wall coverings and painting
- BS 8221-2: 2000 Code of Practice for cleaning and surface repair of buildings. Surface repair of natural stones, brick and terracotta

### Secondary

- BS 8202 Coatings for fire protection of building elements. 2 parts
- BS 8204 Screeds, bases and in-situ floorings [several parts]
- BS EN ISO 28028: 2000 Rubber and/or plastic hose assemblies for airless paint spraying
- CIRIA R174 (1997) New paint systems for the protection of construction steelwork

### Background

- BS 6100:1991 Part 1: Section 1.3, Subsection 1.3.7, Glossary of building and civil engineering terms: Finishes (B)
- CIRIA PR78 (2000) The use of epoxy, polyester and similar reactive polymers in construction, Volume 2: Specification and use of the materials

### Classification

**CAWS** Group M, **CEWS** Class V, **CI/SfB** Code (49)u/v

Read the Introduction before using the following guidelines

## Scope

- Permanent access equipment.
- Temporary access equipment.
- Roped access.
- Hydraulic platforms (cherry picker).
- Fall/arrest systems (latchways).
- New buildings and existing buildings.
- Ladder access.

## Exclusions

- Cleaning of internal spaces, eg atria (see D3).

## Major hazards

Refer to the Introduction for details of accident types and health risks

**Working at height**
Dropped objects and substances during cleaning. Falling out of equipment. Falling off edge of building.

**Collapse and failure**
Provision of safe equipment system for cleaning.

**Hazardous materials**
Aggressive cleaning materials (use and removal), safe removal of waste process materials.

**Weather**
Ropes and equipment becoming unstable, tangled or twisted in the wind. Slippery walking surfaces.

**Hazardous operations**
Repair and maintenance involving cutting, heating gluing or sealing. Unsecured cleaning equipment (eg metal bucket).

**Access**
Safe access and simple operation essential.

Side tabs:
GENERAL PLANNING — A
EXCAVATIONS AND FOUNDATIONS — B
PRIMARY STRUCTURE — C
BUILDING ELEMENTS AND BUILDING SERVICES — D 6
CIVIL ENGINEERING — E

**A** GENERAL PLANNING

**B** EXCAVATIONS AND FOUNDATIONS

**C** PRIMARY STRUCTURE

**D 6** BUILDING ELEMENTS AND BUILDING SERVICES

**E** CIVIL ENGINEERING

## Specific hazard identification

**Possible key considerations:**

- **Building location:** Are these particular access problems? Do the public have to be protected? Will the site preclude using particular equipment or methods? Is the site exposed?

- **Building form:** How is access to cleaning equipment achieved? Will cleaning operations require oversailing the public or another building? What is the form and geometry of the facade to be cleaned? Are there any overhangs to be cleaned? Is the building of exceptional size?

- **Cleaning strategy:** What, if any, specific cleaning requirements for elements of cladding? What is required frequency of cleaning? Will aggressive/harmful cleaning materials be required?

- **Does replacement and maintenance** of element need to be considered?

## Prompts

- Unprotected roof edges
- Trip hazards at roof edges
- Difficult to reach areas
- Special equipment required
- Access to equipment
- Windy site
- Storage of access equipment
- Provision of warning signs

## Hazards consideration in design

| Stage | Considerations and issues | Possible design options to avoid or mitigate hazards identified for cleaning of buildings |
|---|---|---|
| Concept design | • Form of cladding<br>• Cleaning strategy<br>• Cleaning frequency<br>• Materials to be cleaned<br>• Safe working loads<br>• Design life of cladding/finishes<br>• Safe entry/exit<br>• Access to all parts of the facade<br>• Equipment to achieve access require<br>• Review loads from equipment<br>• Power and water supply<br>• Attachment details<br>• Back-up systems<br>• Testing/commission<br>• Service/maintenance | • Consider various types of equipment that can reach all surfaces of the building elevation without dangerous manoeuvres (eg cradle or cherry pickers).<br>• Avoid the use of materials and finishes that require aggressive cleaning materials.<br>• Entry/exit points for cleaning equipment need to be detailed so that dangerous manoeuvres are avoided (eg stepping over the edge of building into cradle).<br>• Consider how cleaning may be eliminated or reduced. |
| Scheme design | | • Develop cleaning strategy to provide full and safe coverage of the whole facade using the preferred method (eg will the stabilising legs of a cherry picker always be on solid ground?).<br>• Develop strategy for dealing with waste products from cleaning operations. |
| Detail design | | • With the equipment selected for cleaning, ensure that the operatives can attach personal protective equipment to secure points everywhere that cleaning and maintenance is required. |

## Examples of risk mitigation (methods of solution)

| ACTION \ ISSUE | Falls from building edge when entering cleaning cradle | Collapse of cherry picker |
|---|---|---|
| **Avoidance**<br>Design to avoid identified hazards but beware of introducing others | Use permanently-installed roof-mounted cleaning equipment provided with luffing and slewing jib, so that access to the cradle can occur away from the roof edge. | Provide a flat, solid, clear access round the base of the building as part of the external landscaping design for the building. |
| **Reduction**<br>Design to reduce identified hazards but beware of increasing others | Use permanently-installed roof-mounted cleaning equipment with a luffing jib, and provide safe entry points guarded by gates and rails, and with tethering points for the cradle. | Provide designated areas round the base of the building that can be accessed and which are flat, solid and clear. |
| **Control**<br>Design to provide acceptable safeguards for all remaining identified hazards | Use permanently-installed roof-mounted cleaning equipment with a luffing jib and provide fall-arrest systems adjacent to cradle access points that can be connected/disconnected when in the cradle. | Specify all-terrain cherry pickers with a known safety record on a variety of surfaces and sub-soil conditions. Provide clear access to the base of the building. |

GENERAL PLANNING **A**

EXCAVATIONS AND FOUNDATIONS **B**

PRIMARY STRUCTURE **C**

BUILDING ELEMENTS AND BUILDING SERVICES **D 6**

CIVIL ENGINEERING **E**

## Examples of risk mitigation (issues addressed at different stages)

An existing office building in the centre of a major city is to be refurbished and reclad. It has a well-maintained track-mounted trolley supporting a hand- operated cradle to clean two facades and a set of fixed davit arms to support a hand-operated cradle for the other facades. The client would like to refurbish this equipment for future use.

| Concept design | Scheme design | Detail design |
|---|---|---|
| Manually - operated equipment will be replaced by electrical operation. Review form and geometry of new cladding to establish performance requirements for new equipment. | Ensure safe access routes into the cradle. | Ensure adequate space to allow safe access for maintenance equipment. |

An existing shopping centre with a glazed roof over the pedestrian malls has been recently purchased by a new landlord. The roof has been cleaned externally by operators using duck boards and ladders. The new owner wants a new purpose-designed roof access system that will allow the glass to be cleaned without anybody having to stand on the roof.

| Concept design | Scheme design | Detail design |
|---|---|---|
| Load limitations on the existing glazing framework mean that a travelling gantry supported off the adjacent structure is required. | The travelling gantry is designed to be built adjacent to the mall glazing, and then run on temporary rails on to the permanent rails each side of the mall. | Design gantry so as to provide a safe working area. |

**A** GENERAL PLANNING

**B** EXCAVATIONS AND FOUNDATIONS

**C** PRIMARY STRUCTURE

**D 6** BUILDING ELEMENTS AND BUILDING SERVICES

**E** CIVIL ENGINEERING

## Related issues

References within this document

| References | Related issues |
|---|---|
| A1 | Surrounding environment may dictate operation times and frequency of cleaning. |
| A4 | Access to site will dictate how machinery is put up and commissioned. |
| A4 | Access to roof areas will dictate sequencing and protection. |
| A4, D2 | Primary structure will dictate type of fixings, type and span of track, weight of access equipment. |
| D1-D5 | Maintenance, repair and replacement strategy of facade/envelope elements needs to be considered with cleaning. |
| | External materials will dictate methods and frequency of cleaning. |

## References for further guidance

Primary general references and background information given in Section 4

### Primary

- BS 5974:1990 Code of practice for temporarily installed suspended scaffolds and access equipment
- BS 6037 Code of practice for the planning, design, installation and use of permanently installed access equipment. 2 parts
- BS 8213-1: 2004 Windows doors and rooflights. Design for safety in use and during cleaning of windows, including door-height windows and roof windows. Code of practice
- CIRIA C652 (2006) Safer surfaces to walk on – reducing the risk of slipping
- CIRIA C611 (2004) Safe access for maintenance and repair
- HSE CIS5 (revised) Temporarily suspended access cradles and platforms
- HSE CIS24 Chemical cleaners

### Secondary

- BS 2830:1994 Specification for suspended access equipment (suspended chairs, traditional steeplejack's seats, work cages, cradles and platforms) for use in the building, engineering construction, steeplejack and cleaning industries
- HSE PM30 Suspended access equipment
- CIRIA SP71 (1989) Graffiti removal and control

### Background

- BS EN 12385-3: 2004 Steel wire ropes. Safety. Information for use and maintenance
- Ashurst, N (1994) Cleaning historic buildings. 2 vols (Donhead)

### Classification

**CAWS** Group A, **CEWS** Class A, **CI/SfB** Code (--)(W2)

Read the Introduction before using the following guidelines

## Scope

- Boiler plant.
- Refrigeration and chiller plant including heat rejection equipment.
- Water treatment plant.
- Air-handling plant.
- Fans and pumps.
- Distribution systems - pipework and ductwork.
- Room units - radiators, fan coils, VAV boxes, etc.
- Gas installations.
- Steam and high temperature hot water installations.
- Smoke ventilation.

## Exclusions

- Specialist containment systems - microbiological cabinets, fume cupboards.
- Systems handling hazardous radiological or biological substances.
- Control and control panels (see D8).

GENERAL PLANNING **A**

EXCAVATIONS AND FOUNDATIONS **B**

PRIMARY STRUCTURE **C**

BUILDING ELEMENTS AND BUILDING SERVICES **D 7**

CIVIL ENGINEERING **E**

## Major hazards

Refer to the Introduction for details of accident types and health risks

**Falling from heights**
Installation, commissioning and maintenance of equipment. Builders work openings

**Manual handling**
Mechanical equipment is generally large and heavy, or simply bulky.

**Hazardous atmospheres/substances**
Explosive gas, dusts or vapours, welding fumes, products of combustion, fine fibres, refrigerants, legionella, etc.

**Hazardous surfaces**
Hot and cold surfaces, projecting parts of equipment (particularly at head and ankle level), sharp edges and ends, tripping and slipping.

**Pressurised plant and systems**
Refrigeration plant, steam, compressed air systems, medical gases. Decommissioning.

**Fixings**
Installation and maintenance of equipment fixing vertical, horizontal.

## D7  Group D – Building elements and building services
### 7 – Mechanical services

A — GENERAL PLANNING

B — EXCAVATIONS AND FOUNDATIONS

C — PRIMARY STRUCTURE

D7 — BUILDING ELEMENTS AND BUILDING SERVICES

E — CIVIL ENGINEERING

### Specific hazard identification

**Possible key considerations:**

- **Working height** - How is the installation, commissioning and maintenance of equipment to be carried out?

- **Access for installation, commissioning and maintenance** - What is the frequency at which tasks are carried out (eg daily, monthly)?

- **Adequate space** - What are the provisions for mechanical or manual handling of equipment in the plant room and along ingress/egress routes?

- **Hazardous substances** - How will use and storage take place in the installation and operation of mechanical services (eg refrigerants ammonia, propane, water treatment chemicals, fine fibres from insulants, microbiological contamination of water services, etc.)?

- **Maintenance** - What are the provisions for the removal and replacement of plant items.

- **Electrical supply to mechanical services**

- **Any others?**

### Prompts

- Rooftop locations
- Tripping hazard - low level pipework in plant rooms
- Hot surfaces - boilers and pipework
- Cold surfaces - liquefied gas pipework
- Sharp surfaces - air-handling plant casing, ductwork cladding
- Projecting parts - valve stems and wheels, head level pipes and ducts, etc.
- Pressure systems
- Manual mechanical handling
- Rotating machinery
- Safety valves
- Fixing details
- Welding vs mechanical fixings

### Hazards consideration in design

| Stage | Considerations and issues | Possible design options to avoid or mitigate hazards identified for mechanical services |
|---|---|---|
| Concept design | • Heating/cooling/ventilation strategy<br>• Plant room sizes and locations<br>• Principal distribution routes<br>• Fuel sources and storage<br>• Existing site services | • A building with good thermal characteristics (eg external envelope) will often reduce the size and complexity of the mechanical services required.<br>• The handling of large plant items and the amount of space can be reduced by considering modular or decentralised plant.<br>• Location of major plant and main distribution routes for pipes and ducts need careful planning and coordination, particularly riser cores to avoid congestion. |
| Scheme design | • Installation strategy<br>• Plant duties and nominal sizes and weights<br>• Pipe and duct distribution<br>• Plant access/egress<br>• Working space for work at all phases<br>• Plant room layouts | • Eliminate or reduce common hazards by thoughtful selection of major plant items - falling from heights (eg low level plant), hazardous substances (eg non-toxic, non-flammable refrigerants), avoidance of pressurised systems (eg low temperature hot water heating systems).<br>• Plan safe handling of plant components along entire access/egress routes. Locate plant rooms to keep these routes as simple as possible, (eg heavy and bulky objects at ground level - large boilers, chillers, storage vessels, etc.). |
| Detail design | • Handling methods for installation, commissioning and maintenance<br>• Temporary access for installation<br>• Materials specification<br>• Storage of plant and materials<br>• Safety interlocks<br>• Asbestos<br>• Hot working | • Layout plant rooms with an understanding of the space needed to install, commission and maintain items of plant. Provide ready access to plant items which require regular/frequent maintenance. Provide permanent guarded stairs and catwalks if this is at high level.<br>• Consider the manual handling tasks at all phases:<br>  - can the task be carried out by one person?<br>  - will mechanical handling devices be needed?<br>• Layout plantroom to avoid tripping hazards and projecting parts by keeping routes free of pipes and ducts. Plan distribution at high level to reduce low level pipework. Provide step-overs for low level pipes where necessary. |

## Examples of risk mitigation (methods of solution)

| ISSUE / ACTION | Working at height | Manual handling |
|---|---|---|
| **Avoidance**<br>Design to avoid identified hazards but beware of introducing others | Design to install and maintain from floor level. | Use modular plant which can be easily dismantled. |
| **Reduction**<br>Design to reduce identified hazards but beware of increasing others | Key components to be accessed from floor level. | Provide sufficient access and space around the plant. |
| **Control**<br>Design to provide acceptable safeguards for all remaining identified hazards | Provide protected catwalks stairs and ladders. | Provide lifting beams for mechanical lifting. |

## Examples of risk mitigation (issues addressed at different stages)

Installation of chiller plant to serve an air conditioned department store with substantial heat gain and long run hours.

| Concept design | Scheme design | Detail design |
|---|---|---|
| Consider using chillers with air-cooled condensers to avoid contamination of condenser water and handling of water treatment chemicals. Consider using HFC refridgerant to avoid using more toxic or inflammable refrigerant options. | Provide adequate space/access for withdrawal of condenser or evaporator tubes. Access/egress routes to allow the safe handling. | Detail plant room layout to reduce the amount of low-level pipe connecting to the evaporator and condenser. Specify lifting beam above chillers to facilitate removal of heavy plant components. Highlight the risk created by refrigerant leakage. |

Distribution pipework and ductwork serving a four pipe fan coil system in a new 10 storey office building.

| Concept design | Scheme design | Detail design |
|---|---|---|
| Consider access space for installation and maintenance at the cores where several services are located, eg ductwork, pipework, electrics, lifts, etc. Segregate service risers to avoid electric shock, fire, explosion hazards. | Co-ordination of horizontal pipework and ductwork in false ceiling voids with structure and other services to provide sufficient space for fixing of brackets for installation and maintenance. Provide clear access to regularly maintained items such as fan coil units, fitters, fire dampers, etc. | Use screwed or flanged connections on pipework to avoid welding. Consider as much prefabrication of pipework and ductwork as possible to reduce the amount work at height. |

GENERAL PLANNING — A

EXCAVATIONS AND FOUNDATIONS — B

PRIMARY STRUCTURE — C

BUILDING ELEMENTS AND BUILDING SERVICES — D 7

CIVIL ENGINEERING — E

# D7 Group D – Building elements and building services
## 7 – Mechanical services

## Related issues

References within this document

| References | Related issues |
|---|---|
| A1 | Surrounding environment determine some effects on and from this work. |
| A4 | Access for working at height in an area of existing plant needs clear access and egress routes/systems. |
| D2 | Roofs are often used to house mechanical plant. |
| D6 | Cleaning of buildings will include and/or use mechanical services. |
| D8 | Electrical services almost always interface with mechanical services. |
| D10 | Lifts, escalators and auto walks may also be associated with mechanical services. |
| E8 | Pipes and cables (forming the external infrastructure) will interface with mechanical services. |

## References for further guidance

Primary general references and background information given in Section 4

### Primary

- Ministry of Defence, Defence Works Functional Standard, Design and Maintenance Guide 08. Space requirements for plant access, operation and maintenance 1996
- BSRIA Technical Note TN 9/92 – Space and weight allowances for building services plant: Inception stage design 1993
- BSRIA Technical Note TN10/92 – Space allowance for building services: Detail design stage 1992
- BSRIA Application Guide 11/92 – Design for maintainability 1992
- CIRIA C611 (2004) Safe access for maintenance and repair
- Department of Health NHS Estates, Health Technical Memorandum (HTM) 2023 – Access and accommodation for engineering services 1995
- Department of Health, NHS Estates, Health Technical Memorandum (HTM) 2040 – The control of legionellae in healthcare premises 1993

### Secondary

- HSE PM5 Automatically controlled steam and hot water boilers
- HSE L8 The control of legionella bacteria in water systems. Approved code of practice and guidance

### Background

- BS 8313:1997 Code of practice for accommodation of building services in ducts

### Classification

**CAWS** Group S&T, **CEWS** Class Z, **CI/SfB** Code (54)/(59)

Read the Introduction before using the following guidelines

## Scope

- HV equipment and transformers.
- LV switchgear and components.
- Uninterruptible power supplies (UPS).
- Generators.
- Lightning protection.
- Fire and security alarm systems.
- Lighting and power cabling.
- Emergency lighting.
- Mechanical plant supplies.

## Exclusions

- Large-scale power generation plant and distribution systems.
- Areas designated as having potentially explosive atmospheres - "hazardous areas".
- Temporary services during construction.

## Major hazards

Refer to the Introduction for details of accident types and health risks

**Confined working spaces**
Installation, maintenance, commissioning.

**Falling from heights**
Installation and maintenance of equipment, falling into pits (eg switchrooms). Builders work openings.

**Manual handling of plant**
Large and heavy switchgear components, transformers, generators, etc.

**Hazardous surfaces**
Hot surfaces, projecting parts of equipment (particularly at head and ankle level), sharp edges and ends, tripping and slipping.

**Hazardous atmospheres/ substances**
Insulating oils from transformers or HV switchgear, acids from batteries, hydrogen from charging batteries, etc.

**Fixings**
Installation and maintenance of fixings for equipment, on walls or in floor/ceiling zones.

# Group D – Building elements and building services
## 8 – Electrical services

## Specific hazard identification

**Possible key considerations:**

- **New build or refurbishment** – identify if the power supply to the building will be "live" during any electrical works?

- **Working height** – how is the installation and maintenance of equipment to be carried out, (eg replacement of lamps)?

- **Access for installation and maintenance** - What is the frequency needed for access to equipment (daily, monthly, etc.)?

- **Adequate space** – what are the provisions for mechanical/ manual handling of equipment in equipment rooms and along access/egress routes through the building?

- **Environment** – could there be flammable or explosive gases or dusts in the space?

- **Maintenance** – what are the provisions for removal and replacement of equipment.

- **Any others ?**

## Prompts

- Equipment located at high level or in false ceiling voids

- Sharp surfaces – electrical tray work and conduits.

- Manual handling (eg removal of switchgear truck)

- Hazardous substances (eg transformer oil)

- Hot surfaces – generator engines and flues

- Enclosure/protection

- Fixing details

## Hazards consideration in design

| Stage | Considerations and issues | Possible design options to avoid or mitigate hazards identified for electrical services |
|---|---|---|
| Concept design | • Electrical supply strategy<br>• Equipment room sizes and locations<br>• Construction requirements - small plant, lighting and plant, UPS<br>• Principal distribution routes<br>• Existing site services<br>• Installation strategy<br>• Equipment and switchgear capacity, nominal sizes and weights | • Maximum size of low-voltage supply may be determined by electricity company. Maintenance of high voltage systems require specially-certificated personnel.<br>• Locate main equipment rooms at outer walls of buildings, where possible, to allow heavy equipment to be placed in one lift from lorry to final position.<br>• Locate equipment away from explosive/flammable atmospheres<br>• Locate principal distribution routes away from plant rooms used by other services (if possible).<br>• Route external cable trenches away from existing routes to avoid coincident excavations.<br>• Avoid whenever possible carrying out electrical work on "live" services. |
| Scheme design | • Main risers and sub-circuit routes<br>• Plant access/egress routes<br>• Switchgear and equipment room layouts<br>• Handling methods for installation and maintenance<br>• Temporary access for installation | • Ensure sufficient space to install largest item of plant safely.<br>• Use dedicated risers and routes for electrical services wherever possible so the electrical installers are not put in danger from other (unfamiliar) services. |
| Detail design | • Materials specification<br>• Separation of services<br>• Earthing and bonding<br>• Enclosure/protection | • Locate equipment with sufficient working space so emergency egress is not obstructed.<br>• Provide lifting beams where heavy parts need to be lifted for maintenance.<br>• Ensure any temporary access for installation does not require electrical contractor to dismantle pipes or rebuild a wall.<br>• Wherever possible, avoid materials that may require special handling or protection during disposal.<br>• Specify all equipment to avoid risk of fire/explosion |

## Examples of risk mitigation (methods of solution)

| ISSUE / ACTION | Hazardous substances | Manual handling during installation |
|---|---|---|
| **Avoidance**<br>Design to avoid identified hazards but beware of introducing others | Consider use of non combustible materials for all electrical equipment to guard against electrical/construction fires. | Design modular switchboards with smaller components. |
| **Reduction**<br>Design to reduce identified hazards but beware of increasing others | Specify fire retardant/low smoke insulants on cables instead of PVC. | Design access routes with sufficient space for mechanical handling devices. |
| **Control**<br>Design to provide acceptable safeguards for all remaining identified hazards | Co-ordinate with other designers to incorporate smoke vents/ventilation in areas where work will take place. | Incorporate lifting beams for electrical gear into primary structure. |

GENERAL PLANNING **A**

EXCAVATIONS AND FOUNDATIONS **B**

PRIMARY STRUCTURE **C**

BUILDING ELEMENTS AND BUILDING SERVICES **D 8**

CIVIL ENGINEERING **E**

## Examples of risk mitigation (issues addressed at different stages)

In designing the mains supply to an urban office building it becomes apparent that building loading requires a new HV supply. The only space available for transformer is in the basement adjacent to the car park area.

| Concept design | Scheme design | Detail design |
|---|---|---|
| Location presents considerable fire risk so use a dry transformer with SF6 or vacuum switchgear. Put all cabling at high level. Access to the new switchroom will be via the car park - incorporate security measures to prevent unauthorised access. | Design to allow HV switchgear and transformer to be installed together in one room. Allow space for removal of HV switchgear and rear access to LV switchgear. | Specify sealed batteries for HV backup to avoid hazard of explosive gasses from charging unsealed batteries. |

Large incoming supply arrangement with multiple transformers and both high voltage and low voltage switchgear.

| Concept design | Scheme design | Detail design |
|---|---|---|
| Consider installing transformers in separate vaults to allow safe working on one while others are still energised. Provide separate rooms for LV and HV switchgear. | Design system with comprehensive electrical interlocking and earthing facilities to ensure no parts can become live unexpectedly. Ensure the interlocks prevent the possibility of earthing live sections or "backfeeding" through the transformers. | Ensure specification of all switchgear includes security provisions, eg padlocks. |

# Group D – Building elements and building services
## 8 – Electrical services

## Related issues

References within this document

| References | Related issues |
|---|---|
| A4 | Access is a crucial issue for installing or maintaining electrical services. |
| D7 | Mechanical services will (almost) always require electrical services. |
| D10 | Lifts and escalators will be electrically driven. |
| E8 | Pipes and cables from external infrastructure will interface with electrical services. |

## References for further guidance

Primary general references and background information given in Section 4

### Primary

- Ministry of Defence, Defence Works Functional Standard, Design and Maintenance Guide 08. Space requirements for plant access, operation and maintenance 1996
- BSRIA Technical Note TN 9/92 – Space and weight allowances for building services plant: Inception stage design 1993
- BSRIA Technical Note TN10/92 – Space allowance for building services: Detail design stage 1992 BSRIA Application Guide 11/92 – Design for maintainability 1992
- CIRIA C611 (2004) Safe access for maintenance and repair
- Department of Health NHS Estates, Health Technical Memorandum (HTM) 2023 – Access and accommodation for engineering services 1995
- Department of Health, NHS Estates, Health Technical Memorandum (HTM) 2040 – The control of legionellae in healthcare premises 1993

### Secondary

- HSE HSR25 Memorandum of guidance on the Electricity at Work Regulations
- BS 8313:1989 Code of practice for accommodation of building services in ducts

### Background

- BS 7671: 2001 Requirements for Electrical Installations: IEE Wiring Regulations. 16th ed
- Stokes, G (2002) A practical guide to the wiring regulations. 3rd ed (Blackwell)

### Classification

**CAWS**  Group V,       **CEWS**  Class Z,       **CI/SfB**  Code (6-)

Read the Introduction before using the following guidelines

## Scope

- Cold water supply.
- Hot water supply.
- Water treatment plant.
- Surface water and foul drainage.
- Waste and refuse disposal systems.
- Above - ground sanitary systems, soil waste and vents.
- Water and gas fire extinguishing systems.

## Exclusions

- Commercial incinerator plant.
- Chemical waste and drainage systems.
- Sewage treatment plants.

GENERAL PLANNING — A

EXCAVATIONS AND FOUNDATIONS — B

PRIMARY STRUCTURE — C

BUILDING ELEMENTS AND BUILDING SERVICES — D 9

CIVIL ENGINEERING — E

## Major hazards

Refer to the Introduction for details of accident types and health risks

**Falls from heights**
During installation, commissioning and maintenance of equipment. Falling into excavations.

**Deep excavations**
Collapse of excavation, working in confined spaces, hazardous gases.

**Access**
Routes to equipmnt.
High level equipment.
Equipment in holes or tunnels.

**Manual handling**
Tanks and other public health plant are generally large and heavy or bulky.

**Hazardous atmospheres/substances**
Explosive atmospheres
(e.g methane), gas, legionella.
Suffocating atmospheres
(eg carbon dioxide).
Poisonous atmospheres
(eg hydrogen sulphide).

**Hazardous surfaces**
Projecting parts of equipment
(particularly at head and ankle level),
sharp edges and ends, tripping and slipping.

# Group D – Building elements and building services
## 9 – Public health services

**D9**

A — GENERAL PLANNING

B — EXCAVATIONS AND FOUNDATIONS

C — PRIMARY STRUCTURE

D9 — BUILDING ELEMENTS AND BUILDING SERVICES

E — CIVIL ENGINEERING

## Specific hazard identification

**Possible key considerations:**

- **Working height** - How is the installation and maintenance of equipment to be carried out?

- **Access for installation and maintenance** - What is the frequency at which tasks are carried out, (eg daily, monthly, etc.)?

- **Adequate space** - What are the provisions for mechanical or manual handling of equipment in the plant room and along access/egress routes through the building?

- **Hazardous substances** - How will the use and storage take place in the installation and operation of mechanical services (eg water treatment chemicals, fine fibres from insulants, etc.)? Is there risk of microbiological contamination of water services?

- **Maintenance** - What are the provisions for the removal and replacement of items of plant?

- **Any others?**

## Prompts

- Roof top locations

- Tripping hazard - low - level pipework in plant rooms

- Hot surfaces - calorifiers and pipework

- Sharp surfaces - cladding

- Projecting parts - valve stems and wheels, head level pipes and ducts, etc.

- Pressure systems

- Manual handling.

- Fixing details

- Purge existing systems

## Hazards consideration in design

| Stage | Considerations and issues | Possible design options to avoid or mitigate hazards identified for public health services |
|---|---|---|
| Concept design | | • Locate bulk water storage tanks in plant rooms with minimum heat gain. Establish principal distribution routes which allow safe manoeuvring of large diameter heavy pipework, during installation and renewal.<br>• Allow access around proposed plant when assessing plant room sizes. These can be refined later.<br>• Establish preliminary information on existing site services. |
| Scheme design | • Water supply/waste/fire extinguishing - systems strategies<br>• Plant room sizes and locations<br>• Principal distribution routes of all services<br>• Water sources and storage<br>• Existing site services<br>• Installation strategy<br>• Plant weights<br>• Plant access/egress routes<br>• Working space for installation<br>• Handling methods for installation and maintenance<br>• Materials specification | • Specify sectional tanks for bulk water storage, for ease of handling.<br>• Allow working space around plant and tanks for installation and maintenance.<br>• Provide working platforms in risers where floor slab is not continued through.<br>• Locate all existing site services before laying out external mains and drainage. Keep excavations clear of existing structures and services.<br>• Minimise depth of excavations |
| Detail design | | • Consider access for lifting equipment which may be required for heavy high level services.<br>• Specify drainage sump pumps which can be maintained at floor level.<br>• Consider (lightweight) plastic materials for larger diameter high-level pipework.<br>• Locate drainage access points where they can be easily and safely maintained.<br>• Locate valves on pipelines at points of safe permanent access.<br>• Ensure safe routes available for replacement of plant.<br>• Holes in GRP tanks to be formed at works to avoid drilling on site. |

# Group D – Building elements and building services
## 9 – Public health services

## Examples of risk mitigation (methods of solution)

| ACTION \ ISSUE | Installing plant at high level | Manual handling during dismantling |
|---|---|---|
| **Avoidance** Design to avoid identified hazards but beware of introducing others | Design to install and maintain plant at floor level. | Use modular plant which can be dismantled into manageable sections. |
| **Reduction** Design to reduce identified hazards but beware of increasing others | Key components to be accessed from floor level. | Provide sufficient access and space around the plant to allow mechanical handling devices to be used. |
| **Control** Design to provide acceptable safeguards for all remaining identified hazards | Provide protected catwalks stairs and ladders to high level plant. | Provide lifting eyes and/or runways for lifting plant with manual assistance. |

## Examples of risk mitigation (issues addressed at different stages)

Large diameter drainage run is to be routed through 5m high plantroom at high level.

| Concept design | Scheme design | Detail design |
|---|---|---|
| Plan route which will have access from below for lifting equipment. This could involve mechanical lifting devices. Avoid routes over arears where future plant might be installed to aid replacement | Consider plastic pipes rather than cast iron, to ease manual handling. For cast iron pipes, specify mechanical joints. | Locate cleaning access doors where they can be accessed from a gantry or permanent catwalk. Where possible, avoid high level cleaning access points by extending access through the floor slab and carry out maintenance from the floor above. |

Drainage outfall from a building is along a main traffic route from office car park.

| Concept design | Scheme design | Detail design |
|---|---|---|
| Route drainage (where possible) below pavement or landscaping. Avoid deep excavation adjacent to existing structures. | Locate manholes away from site roads. Where manholes cannot be avoided in roadway, locate them to one side. If sufficient depth is available, use "side entry" manhole with access shaft in pavement. | In deep manholes use ladders rather than step irons for safer access. Where large heavy duty covers are required, consider multiple covers to reduce manual handling load. Where outfall pipe from manhole is 600mm diameter or greater, fit safety chain across outlet. |

## D9 | Group D – Building elements and building services
## 9 – Public health services

## Related issues

References within this document

| References | Related issues |
|---|---|
| A4 | Access for maintenance and commissioning. |
| B2 | Deep basements and shafts. |
| B3 | Trenches for services. |
| D2 | Roofs - rainwater drainage. |
| D8 | Electrical services connect to equipment and plant. |
| E8 | Pipes and cables. |

## References for further guidance

Primary general references and background information given in Section 4

### Primary

- Ministry of Defence, Defence Works Functional Standard, Design and Maintenance Guide 08. Space requirements for plant access, operation and maintenance 1996
- BSRIA Technical Note TN 9/92 – Space and weight allowances for building services plant: Inception stage design 1993
- BSRIA Technical Note TN10/92 – Space allowance for building services: Detail design stage 1992 BSRIA Application Guide 11/92 – Design for maintainability 1992
- CIRIA C611 (2004) Safe access for maintenance and repair
- Department of Health NHS Estates, Health Technical Memorandum (HTM) 2023 – Access and accommodation for engineering services 1995
- Department of Health, NHS Estates, Health Technical Memorandum (HTM) 2040 – The control of legionellae in healthcare premises 1993
- HSE HSG70 Control of legionellosis

### Secondary

- BS 8313:1989 Code of practice for accommodation of building services in ducts

### Background

- BS EN 752 Drain and sewer systems outside buildings. 7 parts
- Building Regulations 2000. Approved document G: Hygiene
- BS 6700:1997 Specification for design, installation, testing and maintenance of services supplying water for domestic use within buildings and their curtilages
- Institute of Plumbing (2002) Plumbing engineering services design guide (Institute of Plumbing)
- WRc (2001) Sewers for adoption (WRc)
- BS EN 806 Specifications for installations inside buildings conveying water for human consumption. 3 parts

### Classification

**CAWS** Group R&S,     **CEWS** Class Z,     **CI/SfB** Codes (52)/(53)

Read the Introduction before using the following guidelines

## Scope

- Traction lifts.
- Hydraulic lifts.
- Escalators.
- Autowalks.

## Exclusions

- Temporary mobile platforms, scissor lifts.
- General mechanical handling equipment, eg document handling, baggage handling.

## Major hazards

Refer to the Introduction for details of accident types and health risks

**Collapse**
Heavy equipment on un-propped floors.

**Falling from heights**
Falling into pits and shafts. Access to lift motor room.
Installation, commissioning and maintenance of equipment.

**Manual handling**
Large and heavy items of equipment.
Space for installation, commissioning and maintenance.

**Hazardous surfaces**
Projecting parts of equipment (particularly at head and ankle level), sharp edges and ends, tripping and slipping.

**Hazardous substances**
Dusts and vapours, bottled gases, fibrous dust, asbestos, hydraulic oils, etc.
Working in confined spaces.

**Installation**
Noise and vibration, entanglement, trapping, crushing, cutting by moving parts.

GENERAL PLANNING — A

EXCAVATIONS AND FOUNDATIONS — B

PRIMARY STRUCTURE — C

BUILDING ELEMENTS AND BUILDING SERVICES — D 10

CIVIL ENGINEERING — E

**A** GENERAL PLANNING

**B** EXCAVATIONS AND FOUNDATIONS

**C** PRIMARY STRUCTURE

**D 10** BUILDING ELEMENTS AND BUILDING SERVICES

**E** CIVIL ENGINEERING

## Specific hazard identification

**Possible key considerations:**

- **Insulation, isolation, overload protection and earthing of equipment** - What provisions have been made?

- **Working height** - How is the installation and maintenance of equipment to be carried out?

- **Access for installation, commissioning and maintenance** - What is the frequency at which access will be required to equipment (daily, monthly)?

- **Adequate space** - What are provisions for mechanical or manual handling of equipment in equipment rooms and along ingress/egress routes through the building?

- **Maintenance** - What are the provisions for the removal and replacement of items of equipment?

- **Hazardous substances** - What provision has been made for the use, movement and storage of hazardous substances?

- **Any others?**

## Prompts

- Working at high level
- Working in lift shafts
- Sharp surfaces - equipment casing, cladding, etc.
- Manual handling
- Hazardous substances eg hydraulic oil
- Projecting parts - valves, wheels, pipes and ducts
- Fire risks - shafts and machine rooms
- Hot surfaces - motors and hydraulic tanks

## Hazards consideration in design

| Stage | Considerations and issues | Possible design options to avoid or mitigate hazards identified for lifts, escalators, etc. |
|---|---|---|
| Concept design | • Location of lifts and motor rooms<br>• Scope of works<br>• Familiar work<br>• Access<br>• Installation sequences<br>• Lift equipment types<br>• Handling of equipment components<br>• Protection<br>• Installation, commissioning and maintenance procedures<br>• Space for services<br>• Handling of equipment<br>• Finishes<br>• Positioning<br>• Temporary supports | • Consider the time-scale of operation and delivery of plant, avoid duplication of tasks such as striking and re-erection of scaffolding in lift wells.<br>• Consider alternative routes for access. Provide sufficient working space for installation, commissioning and maintenance. |
| Scheme design | | • Specify equipment that is compact in design to allow for easy handling and placing in position.<br>• Allow for suitable permanent/temporary lifting facilities (marked with SWL) for final positioning of plant.<br>• Consider components which are pre-fabricated and delivered to site as packaged units.<br>• Include provision for delivery and handling of components on congested sites. |
| Detail design | | • Allow for future repair or renewal of equipment, by providing suitable lifting access/egress routes for plant and personnel.<br>• Allow for adequate safety harness attachments for personnel working at heights within the lift well.<br>• If mechanical handling is necessary, incorporate into the design provision for mechanical lifting and handling. |

## Examples of risk mitigation (methods of solution)

|  | ISSUE |
|---|---|
| **ACTION** | **Maintenance in confined spaces** |
| **Avoidance** <br> Design to avoid identified hazards but beware of introducing others | Specify long life, sealed components: These to be replaced rather than maintained. |
| **Reduction** <br> Design to reduce identified hazards but beware of increasing others | Specify minimal maintenance components. |
| **Control** <br> Design to provide acceptable safeguards for all remaining identified hazards | Provide sufficient space for maintenance tasks. |

## Examples of risk mitigation (issues addressed at different stages)

The installation of an escalator into a building. A compact escalator system is proposed which can be delivered in one piece to reduce programme requirements.

| Concept design | Scheme design | Detail design |
|---|---|---|
| The overall concept for the method of installation should be planned. | Ensure adequate space allowed for installation. | Further consideration of the sequence of installation. Identify specific hazards due to the building structure. |

Panoramic lift installation to serve a department store

| Concept design | Scheme design | Detail design |
|---|---|---|
| The lift should be designed so that it can be installed in a completed form, or consideration to be given to access/egress routes to allow safe handling of components. | Panoramic lifts use laminated glass, for walls, ceilings and doors. Provision should be made for the safe handling of this material and future cleaning requirements. | The design should allow for safe cleaning of the glass. Allocate one floor, (eg ground level), where all-round access can be arranged. Ensure adequate depth of well to allow safe maintenance. |

GENERAL PLANNING **A**

EXCAVATIONS AND FOUNDATIONS **B**

PRIMARY STRUCTURE **C**

BUILDING ELEMENTS AND BUILDING SERVICES **D 10**

CIVIL ENGINEERING **E**

**A** GENERAL PLANNING

**B** EXCAVATIONS AND FOUNDATIONS

**C** PRIMARY STRUCTURE

**D 10** BUILDING ELEMENTS AND BUILDING SERVICES

**E** CIVIL ENGINEERING

## Related issues

References within this document

| References | Related issues |
|---|---|
| D3 | Roofs may house lift motor rooms. |
| D7 | Mechanical services interact closely with the installation and maintenance of vertical transportation components. |
| D8 | Electrical services need to be considered for the installation and maintenance of lifts and escalators, also emergency lighting. |
| D9 | Public health services - often impinge on the installation and maintenance of lifts and escalators. |
| | Fire engineering needs to be considered for fire-fighting lifts. |

## References for further guidance

Primary general references and background information given in Section 4

### Primary

- BS EN115:1995 Safety rules for the construction and installation of escalators and passenger conveyors
- National Association of Lift Manufacturers. Principles of planning and programming a lift installation
- National Association of Lift Manufacturers/CIBSE – Guidance on the management and maintenance of lifts and escalators

### Secondary

- CIBSE Guide D Transportation in buildings

### Background

- BS 5655 Lifts and service lifts [several parts, including part 6: 2002 Code of practice for the selection and installation of new lifts
- BS 7255: 2001 Code of practice for safe working on lifts
- BS 5588-5: 2004 Fire precautions in the design, construction and use of buildings. Access and facilities for fire-fighting
- Strakosch, G R (1998) The vertical transportation handbook (John Wiley)

### Classification

**CAWS** Group X, **CI//SfB** Code (66)

Read the Introduction before using the following guidelines

## Scope

- Civil engineering construction sites.
- More detail on selected civil engineering operations is given in work sectors E2 to E9.

## Exclusions

- Demolition (see A2)

## Major hazards

Refer to the Introduction for details of accident types and health risks

**Buried/crushed/trapped**
Collapsed excavation of service trench/foundation.
Backfilling in confined space.
Falsework/formwork collapse.

**Slips, trips and falls**
Awkward access/egress.
Inadequate working space.
Unstable platforms.
Untidy workplace.
Slippery/uneven surfaces.

**Health hazards**
Chemicals.
Asbestos.
Gases.
Water-borne diseases and contamination.
Contaminated ground.
Manual handling.

**Machinery and transport**
Site traffic and plant.
Public highway traffic adjacent to site.
Unloading materials and equipment.

**Services**
Power cables (underground and overhead).
Fuel and gas pipelines. Sewers.
High pressure mains water.

**Ground movement**
Landslips, flooding.
Subsidence.
Fractured services.

# Group E – Civil engineering
## 1 – General civil engineering – including small works

**E1**

A — GENERAL PLANNING

B — EXCAVATIONS AND FOUNDATIONS

C — PRIMARY STRUCTURE

D — BUILDING ELEMENTS AND BUILDING SERVICES

E 1 — CIVIL ENGINEERING

## Specific hazard identification

**Possible key considerations:**

- **Site survey** - What is the history of site? Is there contamination from previous use?
- **Ground survey** - What significant foundation problems will be encountered?
- **Working room** - What is the most appropriate plant?
- **Flooding** - What is the likelihood of a flood occurring?
- **Services** - Where are they? What measures to divert or protect?
- **Any others?**

## Prompts

- Previous site use
- Waste disposal
- Access/egress
- Adjacent property
- Adjacent operations
- Construction planning
- Noise/vibration/dust.
- On-site storag
- Confined spaces/ventilation

## Hazards consideration in design

| Stage | Considerations and issues | Possible design options to avoid or mitigate hazards identified for general civil engineering |
|---|---|---|
| Concept design | • Why this infrastructure?<br>• Why this site?<br>• Site history<br>• Affected local buildings<br>• Depth of foundations<br>• Location of services<br>• Access routes<br>• Ground conditions | • Review the practicalities of other layouts or routes with fewer/less serious hazards.<br>• Choose a massing arrangement of structures which will allow wide battered excavations.<br>• Design to consider effect on local environment (eg access/egress, noise and vibration, lighting), not just the convenience and value of the project.<br>• Assess the possible benefits from further site investigation or specialist surveys.<br>• Avoid disturbance of existing services or arrange for diversion of services in advance |
| Scheme design | • Topography<br>• Drainage/hydrology<br>• Working space<br>• Plant/machinery<br>• Excavation support<br>• Spoil/contamination<br>• Drainage | • Consider drainage measures to improve the stability of excavations.<br>• Ensure that construction methods are practical in relation to the working space available.<br>• Design to avoid/limit work in confined spaces. |
| Detail design | • Advance works<br>• Protection of public<br>• Maintenance<br>• Cleaning<br>• Demolition/renewal | • Design to minimise excavation depths.<br>• Consider appropriate methods for groundwater control.<br>• Consider an enabling works contract to protect or divert services.<br>• Include "systems" for future safe working procedures for maintenance, cleaning and possibly demolition phases. |

## Examples of risk mitigation (methods of solution)

| ISSUE<br><br>ACTION | Major services<br>crossing the site | Rights of way |
|---|---|---|
| **Avoidance**<br>Design to avoid identified hazards but beware of introducing others | Plan the location of major buildings/structures to avoid the route of major services. | Avoid established right of way. |
| **Reduction**<br>Design to reduce identified hazards but beware of increasing others | Protect or divert services. | Redirect highways and footpaths temporarily. |
| **Control**<br>Design to provide acceptable safeguards for all remaining identified hazards | Specify suitable identification of services. | On site measures will be managed by Principal Contractor. |

## Examples of risk mitigation (issues addressed at different stages)

A small group of residential dwellings is to be constructed on the site of a disused small sewage works, adjacent to a river. Proposals are required to deal with the residual site contaminants.

| Concept design | Scheme design | Detail design |
|---|---|---|
| Complete site inspection to identify contamination in relation to new dwellings. Identify history and construction records of site. Locate services.<br><br>Consider disposal strategy, tip locations etc | Confirm extent of contamination and ground water details by site investigation.<br>Consider methods to contain/remove contaminants. Identify ground dewatering methods, excavation, drainage requirements, etc. | Develop details for foundations and drainage which minimise ground disturbance. |

A flood alleviation scheme requires surface water storage capacity under a residential street.

| Concept design | Scheme design | Detail design |
|---|---|---|
| Find the optimum balance between cross-sectional area and length of sewer to allow construction access while retaining pedestrian access to the houses.<br><br>Is there an alternative solution that lessens disruption? | Determine the position in the road which minimises the disruption and interfaces with existing services. | Locate penstock taps and main chamber access covers in a traffic island or wide pavement for safer access during maintenance. |

GENERAL PLANNING **A**

EXCAVATIONS AND FOUNDATIONS **B**

PRIMARY STRUCTURE **C**

BUILDING ELEMENTS AND BUILDING SERVICES **D**

CIVIL ENGINEERING **E 1**

## Related issues

References within this document

| References | Related issues |
|---|---|
| A1 | Local environment protection is required from the hazards associated with any construction work. |
| A2 | Site clearance and demolition |
| A3 | Ground investigations should be related to the project to be constructed. |
| A4 | Access/egress routes may affect the site and hence the construction materials to be used and the frequency of deliveries. |
| A5 | Site layout will be determined by the project to be constructed on the site available and plant to be used. If site restricted, hazards of construction could be accentuated. |
| C1-C4 | Concrete construction |
| C5,C6 | Structural Steelwork construction |
| E2,E3 | Railways/roads/water, adjacent construction work should include safe distances and suitable protection for persons on site. |

## References for further guidance

Primary general references and background information given in Section 4

### Primary

- CIRIA SP57 (1988) Handling of materials on site
- CIRIA R97 (1992) Trenching practice
- HSE HSG47 Avoiding danger from underground services
- HSE GS6 Avoidance of danger from overhead electric power lines
- HSE HSG66 Protection of workers and the general public during the development of contaminated land
- HSE CIS36 Silica

### Secondary

- HSE INDG258 Safe work in confined spaces
- HSE GS289 Parts 1 to 4 health and safety in demolition work
- HSE GS28 Parts 1 to 4 Safe erection of structures
- CIRIA R130 (1993) Methane: its occurrence and hazards in construction
- CIRIA C515 (2000) Groundwater control – design and practice
- CIRIA R182 (1998) Pumping stations – design for improved buildability and maintenance
- CIRIA R185 (1999) The observational method in ground engineering: principles and applications
- CIRIA SP32 (1984) Construction over abandoned mineworkings
- HSE MDHS100 Surveying sampling and assessment of asbestos coating materials

### Background

- Doran, D (2004) Site engineers manual (Whittles)
- BS 6031:1981 Code of practice for earthworks
- BS 8002:1994 Earth retaining structures
- Tomlinson, M J (2001) Foundation design and construction. 7th ed (Prentice Hall)
- Pitman, P (2001) External works and drainage: a practical guide (Spon)

### Classification

**CEWS** Classes A-Z, **CI/SfB** Code (--)1

Read the Introduction before using the following guidelines

## Scope

- Existing roads - motorways, dual carriageways, all-purpose roads in rural, urban and city centre locations.
- New road construction, including motorway widening.
- More detail on selected civil engineering operations is given in E1 and E3 to E8.

## Exclusions

- Roads in tunnels.
- Roads on viaducts.
- Temporary roads.

## Major hazards

Refer to the Introduction for details of accident types and health risks

**Traffic**
Working adjacent to live traffic. Traffic management in temporary conditions. Intrusion of runaway vehicles.

**Falls**
Equipment dropped from overhead structure/top of retaining wall. Falls into route of traffic.

**Plant and machinery**
Collisions between construction plant, highway traffic and pedestrians. Crossing and slewing over the highway.

**Services**
Excavation of pipes, drains and cables. Collision with overhead cables.

**Buried/crushed/trapped**
Collapse of excavation for drainage or services.
Landslip triggered by excavation near toe of batter/surcharge.

**Health hazards**
Damaged hearing.
Vibration white finger.
Inhalation of dust and solvents.
Contaminated land.

GENERAL PLANNING **A**

EXCAVATIONS AND FOUNDATIONS **B**

PRIMARY STRUCTURE **C**

BUILDING ELEMENTS AND BUILDING SERVICES **D**

CIVIL ENGINEERING **E 2**

**A**   GENERAL PLANNING

**B**   EXCAVATIONS AND FOUNDATIONS

**C**   PRIMARY STRUCTURE

**D**   BUILDING ELEMENTS AND BUILDING SERVICES

**E 2**   CIVIL ENGINEERING

## Specific hazard identification

**Possible key considerations:**

- **Site survey** - What site contamination is present?
- **Ground investigation** - What water table and slope stability problems exist?
- **Access** - How is safe access and egress provided?
- **Working room** - How can sufficient space for safety zones and plant/equipment be allocated?
- **Traffic management** - How can the design assist traffic and pedestrian management?
- **General public** - What site security arrangements are required?
- **Services - Location?** What measures are needed to protect?
- **Night working -** Where work has to be carried out at night, is there need for any spoecial measures such as lighting?
- **Any others?**

## Prompts

- Access Routes
- Traffic diversions
- Lane closures/signage
- Deliveries/waste disposal
- Utilities/services
- Weather
- Road/street lighting
- Protect pedestrians
- Visibility

## Hazards consideration in design

| Stage | Considerations and issues | Possible design options to avoid or mitigate hazards identified for working adjacent to and maintaining roads |
|---|---|---|
| Concept design | • Site history<br>• Urban/rural location<br>• Access routes<br>• Services<br>• Hydrology<br>• Lane rental | • Consider whether further soil testing/investigation will enable a better prediction of temporary slope stability.<br>• Consider location of major overhead or underground services with respect to expected working methods.<br>• The route location and type of road should be considered in relation to safe access and delivery of materials to the site. |
| Scheme design | • Ground conditions<br>• Road geometry<br>• Drainage<br>• Plant and machinery<br>• Working space<br>• Sequencing<br>• Advance works<br>• Traffic management<br>• Interaction with existing traffic | • For easier access and movement of machinery, consider advance drainage works, watercourse diversions, etc.<br>• Check that the chosen temporary diversion of traffic causes the least trouble elsewhere.<br>• Design to facilitate staged construction, so that traffic is not diverted elsewhere. |
| Detail design | • Pavement<br>• Earthworks<br>• Noise<br>• Maintenance<br>• Night working | • Avoid the (temporary) diversion of services in advance of works commencing.<br>• Traffic management measures, temporary signage and lighting to be incorporated into partially complete works.<br>• Design to reduce frequency of maintenance, particularly for the more heavily trafficked routes.<br>• Programme the contract periods to avoid seasonal peak traffic flows. |

## Examples of risk mitigation (methods of solution)

| ISSUE / ACTION | Working adjacent to high speed traffic | Land slide/ embankment slip |
|---|---|---|
| **Avoidance** Design to avoid identified hazards but beware of introducing others | Divert all traffic or close one carriageway. | Minimum or zero excavation required by using piled foundations and setting the structure at a higher level. |
| **Reduction** Design to reduce identified hazards but beware of increasing others | Divert Heavy Goods Vehicles (HGV) only. Add a lane closure to create a buffer zone. | Grade the embankment or cutting to a shallower angle before excavation for other works. |
| **Control** Design to provide acceptable safeguards for all remaining identified hazards | Specify concrete barriers. | Stabilise the slope by contingency methods (such as soil nailing) and drainage, as required in response to movement monitoring. |

## Examples of risk mitigation (issues addressed at different stages)

A stretch of uneven road surface requires emergency repair.

| Concept design | Scheme design | Detail design |
|---|---|---|
| The exposure of workers was assessed for both temporary repair and complete carriageway reconstruction. Possible road closure periods identified. | Investigations organised ahead of repairs to reduce the possibility of extra unforeseen works. Roadwork contracts on neighbouring routes were accelerated or delayed to minimise overall disruption. | Materials were chosen which could be laid in narrow strips to give maximum flexibility of construction planning. |

A single carriageway is to be converted to a two-lane dual carriageway.

| Concept design | Scheme design | Detail design |
|---|---|---|
| Consider new routes on separate land, parallel land take or confining work to existing corridor. | Route details to consider safe access points for plant and operatives. | New road lighting designed to reduce the need for temporary lighting during construction. |

GENERAL PLANNING **A**

EXCAVATIONS AND FOUNDATIONS **B**

PRIMARY STRUCTURE **C**

BUILDING ELEMENTS AND BUILDING SERVICES **D**

CIVIL ENGINEERING **E2**

**A** GENERAL PLANNING

**B** EXCAVATIONS AND FOUNDATIONS

**C** PRIMARY STRUCTURE

**D** BUILDING ELEMENTS AND BUILDING SERVICES

**E 2** CIVIL ENGINEERING

## Related issues

References within this document

| References | Related issues |
|---|---|
| A1 | Local environment should be protected from the hazards associated with roadworks. |
| A3 | Ground investigations should include testing for toxic materials, soil density and gases, as well as stability and groundwater details. |
| A4 | Access/egress routes at the site should be kept clean, clear and suitable for emergency services. |
| A5 | Site layout should be suitable for the working space available and plant anticipated to be used on the site. |
| C1-C4 | Concrete materials brought to site in bulk for batching will require designated storage and batching areas. |
| C5,C6 | Special Access routes for large prefabricated elements need to be planned. |
| E1 | General civil engineering often involves working adjacent to roads |
| E4,E5 | Bridge construction and maintenance |
| E6,E7 | Working near water introduces the hazards of drowning and flooding. |
| E8 | Pipes and cables are most often installed adjacent to roads. |

## References for further guidance

Primary general references and background information given in Section 4

### Primary

- DfT (2006) Traffic Signs Manual chapter 8: roadworks and temporary situations. 2 parts
- HA/CSS/HSE Guidance for safer temporary traffic management – as maintained on HA website
- HA/CSS/HSE Temporary traffic management on high speed roads – good working practice – as maintained on the Highways Agency website
- HSE CIS36 – Silica
- DTLR (2001) Safety at street works and road works: a code of practice (TSO)

### Secondary

- CIRIA R113 (1986) Control of a groundwater for temporary works

### Background

- Wignall, A (1999) Roadwork theory and practice (Butterworth Heinemann)

### Classification

**CEWS** Class R, **CI/SfB** Code (--)12

Read the Introduction before using the following guidelines

## Scope

- Working adjacent to, and over operational railways.
- Maintenance work on operational railways.
- More detail on selected civil engineering operations is given in work sectors E1, E2 and E4 to E6.

**Note:** Extensive and strict procedures apply when working in connection with operational railways to ensure safety of the workers and general public. The clear definition of the work area with respect to the line is of paramount importance. This will be determined by the respective operator (eg Railtrack, London Underground Ltd, Docklands Light Railway, etc).

## Exclusions

- Railways in tunnels.
- Maintenance depots.
- Specialist trackwork and electrification work.
- Private railways.

## Major hazards

Refer to the Introduction for details of accident types and health risks

**Struck by moving trains**
Organisation of personnel and material handling not in accordance with established safety procedures.

**Lifting failures**
Electrocution (overhead or third rail). Damage to signals, signal controls and communications.

**Ground instability**
Rock falls into cuttings.
Embankment slips.

**Trains collide with plant**
Encroachment into permanent way envelope by plant/machinery.
Dropped equipment/components.

**Falls, trips and slips**
Bridge maintenance.
Uneven surfaces.
Steep cuttings and embankments.
Access to services.

**Health hazards**
Noise and vibration.
Contaminated land.
Asbestos, oils.

A — GENERAL PLANNING

B — EXCAVATIONS AND FOUNDATIONS

C — PRIMARY STRUCTURE

D — BUILDING ELEMENTS AND BUILDING SERVICES

E 3 — CIVIL ENGINEERING

## Specific hazard identification

**Possible key considerations:**

- **Electricity** - How are lines electrified (overhead and electric, 3rd or 4th Rail)?
- **Working Space** - What size of plant is to be used? Is there sufficient space?
- **Site survey/Records** - Where are cable, signals cabinets, other railway furniture located?
- **Track geometry** - How will this affect work methods?
- **Train movement** - What train movements have to be maintained?
- **Track possessions** - Will possessions be necessary or possible?
- **Track operator** - What are the requirements of the operator?
- **Operations/windows** - Track possession or full closure?
- **Night working** - Where work has to be carried out at night, is there need for any spoecial measures such as lighting?
- **Any others?**

## Prompts

- Track working rules and procedures
- Codes of practice
- Contamination
- Protection of public
- Noise/vibration
- Weather/temperature
- Material storage
- Emergency procedures
- Access
- General public
- Visibility

## Hazards consideration in design

| Stage | Considerations and issues | Possible design options to avoid or mitigate hazards identified for working adjacent to, and working on railways |
|---|---|---|
| Concept design | • Historical records<br>• Site access restrictions<br>• Underground and overground services<br>• Maintenance<br>• Location | • Consider design options in which the proximity of the railway has least effect.<br>• The type and frequency of rail traffic may prohibit or restrict certain methods of construction.<br>• Design for minimum track possessions or consider full closure with train diversions.<br>• Check whether the safety of rail passengers will be impaired in anyway. Ensure separation of public and construction work. |
| Scheme design | • Working space<br>• Ground conditions<br>• Drainage<br>• Night working<br>• Access<br>• Working at stations<br>• Safe refuge areas<br>• Disposal of waste | • Examine the possibility of modification to cuttings and embankments to improve working space or storage areas.<br>• Consider night working and removal of power supply to overhead lines or electrified rails.<br>• Determine the activities which require track possession and for how long.<br>• Provide access to control boxes etc. other than along the track.<br>• Allow for frequent areas of safety alongside the track. |
| Detail design | • Cable protection<br>• Track possessions<br>• Delivery of materials<br>• General Public<br>• Other transport systems | • Consider the protection and/or duplication of signalling. equipment, controls and communications.<br>• Match packages of work and their content to planned periods of track possession.<br>• Highlight options for the separation of general public and work on site. |

## Examples of risk mitigation (methods of solution)

| ACTION / ISSUE | Facility close to overhead electrification lines | Installation of inspection boxes for maintenance |
|---|---|---|
| **Avoidance** Design to avoid identified hazards but beware of introducing others | Locate facility away from overhead electric lines | Position boxes where access can be obtained away from track side |
| **Reduction** Design to reduce identified hazards but beware of increasing others | Design components to require small cranes. | Provide defined and guarded access ways to boxes alongside trackside |
| **Control** Design to provide acceptable safeguards for all remaining identified hazards | Outline erection sequences assumed. Place goal posts. | |

## Examples of risk mitigation (issues addressed at different stages)

A distribution warehouse for a mail-order company is to be built on a long rectangular plot of land close to an overhead electrified railway.

| Concept design | Scheme design | Detail design |
|---|---|---|
| Design the access road to the warehouse to abut the railway land. | The designer favours more and shallower piles rather than fewer deeper piles (taller rigs). The deeper drains will be routed furthest from the railway land. | |

A road crosses over a non-electrified railway line. Routine maintenance inspections of the bridge have identified that remedial works are necessary to the parapets of the bridge.

| Concept design | Scheme design | Detail design |
|---|---|---|
| Consider track status and whether overnight working is necessary. Consult with controllers of track on requirements | Identify methods which do not encroach onto the track, even for track possession periods. | Ensure that the methods of repair have set-up, preparation, and curing periods which are compatible with the times of possession. |

GENERAL PLANNING — A

EXCAVATIONS AND FOUNDATIONS — B

PRIMARY STRUCTURE — C

BUILDING ELEMENTS AND BUILDING SERVICES — D

CIVIL ENGINEERING — E 3

## Related issues

References within this document

| References | Related issues |
|---|---|
| A2 | Site clearance activities will need to consider the local environment. |
| A4 | Access/egress routes will also be determined by local considerations eg roads, urban/rural site interface with general public and other transport systems. |
| A5 | Site layout will be determined by working space available and track safety measures required. |
| B1-B3 | Excavation and earthworks will need to consider effects on drainage and permanent way track stability. |
| C1-C6 | Construction materials may require special routes to site and careful consideration with respect to site storage. |
| D7-D9 | Services for power conducting and signalling systems need careful attention. |
| E1 | Working space restrictions especially on small sites accentuate problems. |

## References for further guidance

Primary general references and background information given in Section 4

### Primary

- Railway Safety & Standards Board. Railway Group Standards
- Network Rail RT3170 (2005) Track Safety Handbook
- Railway Safety GE/RT8067 (2002) Personal track safety

### Secondary

- Railway Safety GI/RT7003 (2001) Management of construction work in the operational railway environment

### Background

- Permanent Way Institution. British railway track. 7th ed. 12 vols, not all yet published
- Esveld, C (2001) Modern Railway Track. 2nd ed (MRT Productions)

### Classification

**CEWS** Class A,     **CI/SfB** Code (--)11

Read the Introduction before using the following guidelines

## Scope

- Bridges for and over/under roads, railways, rivers, canals.
  (Includes footbridges, subways, farm bridges, temporary bridges.)
- Bridge strengthening and major repairs.

## Exclusions

- Tunnels, piped watercourse, corrugated metal culverts.

## Major hazards

Refer to the Introduction for details of accident types and health risks

**Falls**
Work at height.
Inadequate access.

**Intrusions**
Collapse of foundation excavation/or cofferdam.
Embankment slip.
Highway traffic.

**Services**
Overhead and underground cables.
Pipes and cables concealed in the bridge deck.

**Buried/crushed/trapped**
Collapse of permanent and temporary work during construction.
Trapped under permanent bearing.

**Plant and machinery**
Struck by plant, or materials and units being slewed into position.
Failure of jack or cables during tensioning.

**Health hazards**
Concrete additives.
Liquid applied waterproofers.
Hot bitumen.
Contaminated land.

## E4

# Group E – Civil engineering
## 4 – Bridge construction

**A** GENERAL PLANNING

**B** EXCAVATIONS AND FOUNDATIONS

**C** PRIMARY STRUCTURE

**D** BUILDING ELEMENTS AND BUILDING SERVICES

**E 4** CIVIL ENGINEERING

## Specific hazard identification

**Possible key considerations:**

- **Stability** - What procedures required for safe erection?
- **Site investigation** - What hazards do ground conditions present?
- **Access/working room** - Where can materials be stored to provide clear/safe access and working space?
- **Services** - Is the site affected by overhead and underground services? Where are the services?
- **The spanned facility** - What particular safety procedures need to be addressed for whatever is crossed?
- **Access** - What facility is required for future maintenance?
- **Public** - What protection methods are required?
- **Any others?**

## Prompts

- Site history
- Access routes
- Materials delivery/storage/use
- Contaminated land
- Adjacent structures
- Demolition
- Future maintenance
- Waste disposal

## Hazards consideration in design

| Stage | Considerations and issues | Possible design options to avoid or mitigate hazards identified for bridge construction |
|---|---|---|
| Concept design | • Is a bridge necessary?<br>• Local issues affecting design<br>• Access to site<br>• Overhead/underground services<br>• Ground conditions | • Consider reducing the number of piers by increasing the length of spans.<br>• Is the desired profile for wind resistance more safely achieved by shaping the off-site prefabricated structural units or by on-site addition of cladding?<br>• Location of abutment to respect local ground conditions as well as alignment of routes under and over.<br>• Choose structural form and material with respect to future |
| Scheme design | • Future maintenance.<br>• Demolition<br>• Sequence of construction<br>• Foundations<br>• Working space<br>• Ground contamination<br>• Hydrology<br>• Services | maintenance and appropriateness of prefabrication.<br>• Favour minimum depth of excavation for bridge foundations.<br>• Reduce groundwater problems (that may cause instability) by appropriate drainage measures.<br>• Avoid the need to (temporarily) divert services in advance of construction.<br>• Consider what temporary works are expected and what construction methods are excluded by the nature of the site. |
| Detail design | • Materials delivery<br>• Storage<br>• Excavation<br>• Temporary structural supports<br>• Lifting measures | • More durable design solutions will reduce the frequency of future maintenance.<br>• Ensure that prefabricated components can be handled practically by choosing symmetrical forms and incorporating lifting points.<br>• Assess whether prefabricated units could incorporate the permanent barriers.<br>• Include facilities for safe access to carry out future inspections and maintenance. |

## Examples of risk mitigation (methods of solution)

| ISSUE<br><br>ACTION | Vehicle collision with abutment works | Access gantries for maintenance |
|---|---|---|
| **Avoidance**<br>Design to avoid identified hazards but beware of introducing others | Increase span of bridge to obviate need for abutments or allow them further away from road. | Not needed because a permanent means of access is incorporated into the design. |
| **Reduction**<br>Design to reduce identified hazards but beware of increasing others | Design a permanent barrier to be installed before abutment work commences and to remain effective throughout construction. | Access routes provided for all internal inspections and all external surfaces are reachable by lorry-mounted equipment. |
| **Control**<br>Design to provide acceptable safeguards for all remaining identified hazards | Reduce vehicle speed and/or change routes by traffic control eg narrow lanes, closed lanes, contra-flows etc. | Brackets and holes provided at frequent intervals sufficient to construct temporary access to all areas. |

## Examples of risk mitigation (issues addressed at different stages)

An existing road bridge is to be reconstructed. The duration of the works is expected to be twelve months. The location is urban. Local road and pedestrian traffic at peak times is considerable. The bridge crosses a canal.

| Concept design | Scheme design | Detail design |
|---|---|---|
| What services use the bridge as a crossing? Consider temporary closures and partial closures. Determine usage of canal and tow path. | Co-ordinate the location of a temporary bridge for service diversions, and pedestrian traffic. Bored pile design less likely to disturb canal than driven piles or large excavations. | Consider/provide suitable solution for traffic diversions and public access to properties on each side. |

An existing motorway bridge is to be symmetrically widened to accommodate an additional traffic lane on either side.

| Concept design | Scheme design | Detail design |
|---|---|---|
| Consider construction history and as-built drawings. Assess structure to determine necessary modification or demolition and replace. Additional lane and new hard shoulder? Traffic and access constraints. | Identify methods to reduce worker/road traffic conflict. Consider disruption to road traffic and identify an acceptable sequence of construction. | Identify maintenance and repair strategy for bridge. Review assumed construction methods and sequences. |

## Related issues

References within this document

| References | Related issues |
|---|---|
| A1 | Local environment requires protection from the hazards associated with any construction work. |
| A2 | Site clearance will involve access and demolition problems. |
| A3 | Ground investigations should be comprehensive to allow alternative methods of construction to be investigated. |
| A4 | Access/egress routes may affect the construction method and materials to be used at the site as well as site security and protection of the public. |
| A5,E1 | Site layout working room will determine construction methods and appropriate construction plant to be used. |
| B1,B3 | Excavation/foundation will need to consider drainage and stability problems. |
| C1-C4 | Concrete construction hazards will arise in the foundations, abutments and spanning members. |
| C5,C6 | Structural steelwork construction hazards will arise mainly for the spanning members. |
| C7 | Masonry hazards will arise when facing abutments with stonework or similar. |
| C8 | Timber hazards will arise for small span bridges. |
| E6 | Working over/near water will add additional hazards for bridge construction. |

## References for further guidance

Primary general references and background information given in Section 4

### Primary

- HSE GS28 Parts 1 to 4 Safe erection of structures
- CIRIA R155 (1996) Bridges – design for improved buildability
- CIRIA C656 (2006) Masonry arch bridges: condition appraisal and remedial treatment

### Secondary

- CIRIA SP57 (1988) Handling of materials on site
- Ryall, M J (2000) Bridge management 4: Inspection, maintenance, assessment and repair (Thomas Telford)

### Background

- Ryall, M J (2000) Manual of bridge engineering (Thomas Telford)
- Pritchard, B (1992) Bridge design for economy and durability (Thomas Telford)
- CIRIA SP95 (1993) The design and construction of sheet-piled cofferdams
- Highways Agency: Design Manual for roads and bridges
- SCI Publication 318 (2004) Design guide for steel railway bridges
- Clark, L A (1983) Concrete bridge design to BS 5400 (Construction Press)

### Classification

**CI/SfB** Code (--)182

Read the Introduction before using the following guidelines

## Scope

- Existing bridges for and over roads, railways, aqueducts, viaducts, footbridges, farm bridges, subways.

  (Maintenance to include: inspection surveys, monitoring, cleaning, and painting.)

## Exclusions

- Tunnels, CM culverts, piped watercourses.
- Bridge strengthening and repairs (see E4).

A GENERAL PLANNING

B EXCAVATIONS AND FOUNDATIONS

C PRIMARY STRUCTURE

D BUILDING ELEMENTS AND BUILDING SERVICES

E 5 CIVIL ENGINEERING

## Major hazards

Refer to the Introduction for details of accident types and health risks

**Falls**
Awkward access.
Unsafe place of work.
Difficult working position.

**Plant and machinery**
Use of small tools in restricted circumstances.
Struck by access gantries and lifting/slewing operations.

**Traffic**
Working adjacent road/ railway traffic.
Large vehicles close to work areas under the bridge. Pedestrian routes.

**Services**
Cables and pipes concealed in the bridge deck.
Electrified rails and overhead cables.

**Health hazards**
Waterproofing primers.
Paint and solvents. Dust. Skin irritants and allergens.

**Asphyxiation**
Working in confined spaces. Harmful gases.

## E5

# Group E – Civil engineering
# 5 – Bridge maintenance

**A** — GENERAL PLANNING

**B** — EXCAVATIONS AND FOUNDATIONS

**C** — PRIMARY STRUCTURE

**D** — BUILDING ELEMENTS AND BUILDING SERVICES

**E5** — CIVIL ENGINEERING

## Specific hazard identification

**Possible key considerations:**

- **Bridge location** - What is the bridge type? What does it cross (eg water, road or railway?
- **Bridge details** - Clearance, structural form, prestressed elements?
- **Access/working room** - What are suitable plant and equipment for inspection and maintenance?
- **Services** - What services exist within/without structure to be accommodated? Protection/access?
- **Environment** - Will the site or use of the bridge exclude using particular plant or materials?
- **Any others?**

## Prompts

- Health and safety file?
- Construction history
- Drawings/manuals
- Ground conditions
- Working platforms
- Confined spaces
- Temporary structures
- Weather conditions
- Services
- Repair materials

## Hazards consideration in design

| Stage | Considerations and issues | Possible design options to avoid or mitigate hazards identified for bridge maintenance |
|---|---|---|
| Concept design | | • Review the implications of deferring the maintenance work.<br>• Check demolition and replacement as an alternative to frequent maintenance.<br>• If the extent and scope of work is uncertain, consider further inspections before advancing the design. |
| Scheme design | • Bridge type<br>• Access<br>• Environment<br>• Working space<br>• Possessions<br>• Inspection<br>• Ground investigation<br>• Hard standing/platform locations<br>• Fixtures for access assistance<br>• Sequence/phasing<br>• Temporary work<br>• Hazardous materials<br>• Plant and machinery<br>• Services<br>• Task lighting and visibility | • If the work is weather sensitive, define or revise the programme accordingly.<br>• Ensure that the preferred solution takes advantage of new developments in access equipment - eg lorry-mounted booms for access to bridge soffits. |
| Detail design | | • Favour the selection of repair processes with less noise, dust, waste and harmful substances.<br>• Select preparation and application methods which use remotely controlled equipment. |

## Examples of risk mitigation (methods of solution)

| ACTION \ ISSUE | Provide temporary access | Hazardous substances |
|---|---|---|
| **Avoidance**<br>Design to avoid identified hazards but beware of introducing others | Use robots, CCTV, and electronic survey methods for remote inspection. | Exclude the use of materials, chemicals and solvents with known risks to health. |
| **Reduction**<br>Design to reduce identified hazards but beware of increasing others | Use lorry-mounted access platforms to minimise the time period of men and equipment on site. | Hazardous substances only allowed if they significantly extend the period to first maintenance and reduce frequency of maintenance thereafter. |
| **Control**<br>Design to provide acceptable safeguards for all remaining identified hazards | Divert traffic, calm traffic, provide barriers and buffer zones around the erection of traditional scaffolding. | Control of hazardous substances will be managed by principal contractor. |

## Examples of risk mitigation (issues addressed at different stages)

There is serious spalling on the soffit of a concrete bridge deck over a canal.

| Concept design | Scheme design | Detail design |
|---|---|---|
| Determine whether the work can be effected without compromising the integrity of the bridge. Consider the practicality of using a temporary deck or pontoon for easy access. | Specify lane closures to reduce maximum load on bridge. | Select materials and methods which will allow the works to be broken down into smaller controlled areas. |

Waterproofing for a road bridge deck is to minimise water ingress and hence road salt attack in order to reduce maintenance and the hazards associated with working at height.

| Concept design | Scheme design | Detail design |
|---|---|---|
| Maximise deck cross fall with drainage facility to cater for large rainfall events. Plan bridge closure and/or traffic diversions. | Consider appropriate waterproofing options (sheet materials, liquid coatings, impregnation) and assess their inherent risks to health. | Design for eventual replacement/ ease of repair of waterproofing system. |

GENERAL PLANNING **A**

EXCAVATIONS AND FOUNDATIONS **B**

PRIMARY STRUCTURE **C**

BUILDING ELEMENTS AND BUILDING SERVICES **D**

CIVIL ENGINEERING **E5**

## Related issues

References within this document

| References | Related issues |
|---|---|
| A1 | Local environment is affected by maintenance work which invariably disrupts pedestrian and road traffic movements. |
| A2 | Site clearance relates to safe access and storage of materials. |
| A4 | Access/egress to the structure is one of the most important safety aspects of bridge maintenance. Access constraints may also dictate plant/machinery to be used. |
| A5,E1 | Site location/working space will dictate equipment and materials to be used. Confined working accentuates and creates hazards. |
| B1 | Excavation will need to consider effect on drainage and bridge stability. |
| C1-C6 | Construction materials have inherent properties and their method of application may be hazardous to health. |
| E6 | Working over/near water will add hazards to bridge maintenance. |

## References for further guidance

Primary general references and background information given in Section 4

### Primary

- Parke, G A R (2005) Bridge management 5 (Thomas Telford) and the four earlier conferences
- Ryall, M J (2001) Bridge management (Butterworth Heinemann)
- IStructE (1996) The operation and maintenance of bridge access gantries and runways [2007 edition in preparation]

### Secondary

- HSE INDG258 Safe work in confined spaces
- CIRIA R155 (1996) Bridges: design for improved buildability

### Background

- Highways Agency: Design manual for roads and bridges

### Classification

**CI/SfB** Code (--)182 (W2)

Read the Introduction before using the following guidelines

## Scope

- Inland and coastal waters.

  Including: watercourses, (rivers, canals, ditches), lakes, reservoirs, ponds, tanks, docks, wharves, estuaries, harbours.

## Exclusions

- Work in offshore waters.

## Major hazards

Refer to the Introduction for details of accident types and health risks

**Immersion**
Cold water shock.
Hypothermia.
Fatigue.
Drowning.

**Moving water**
River currents, scour.
Tidal movements.
Flood water.

**Services**
Electrocution/explosion,
(power cables in water).

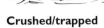

**Health hazards**
Water-borne diseases
(eg Weil's Disease).
Contaminated water.
Chemicals.

**Crushed/trapped**
Impact by boats and pontoons.
Struck by plant or slewed materials and
equipment.

**Falls**
Slipping on wet surfaces.
Awkward access.
Unstable platforms.

## Specific hazard identification

**Possible key considerations:**

- **Site survey** - What are tidal movements? Any locks, weirs and sluices, etc?
- **Access/egress** - What is required to make safe with sufficient protection?
- **Working room** - What plant to use? Where to locate plant and materials?
- **Location** - What is the nature of the water (running or still)? Is it sea, river, canal, lake? What is depth and tidal range?
- **Working level** - What are the methods to safeguard falling from height? What emergency procedures are necessary?
- **Any others?**

## Prompts

- Guard rails/barriers
- Protection of public
- Contamination
- Illumination
- Weather conditions
- Seasonal changes

## Hazards consideration in design

| Stage | Considerations and issues | Possible design options to avoid or mitigate hazards identified for working over/near water |
|---|---|---|
| Concept design | • Site survey<br>• Water type/depth<br>• Location<br>• Services<br>• Geotechnical investigation<br>• Working space<br>• Contamination<br>• Safe access<br>• Advance works (services, drainage)<br>• Excavations<br>• Emergency procedures<br>• Sequence of operations | • Choose a prefabricated construction to avoid/minimise fabrication over water.<br>• Divert or exclude the water by dams and pumping.<br>• Consider temporary infilling or a grillage of pontoons to exclude or isolate the water.<br>• Check whether working space or bed conditions exclude any construction methods. |
| Scheme design | | • Ascertain a programme and design for the works to be carried out at low tide only.<br>• Maximise the types of component which could be prefabricated.<br>• Examine sequences of working to minimise period of exposure. |
| Detail design | | • Select more durable materials and finishes for surfaces which require maintenance access over water (i.e. fewer visits required).<br>• New works to include provision for future maintenance access where possible. |

## Examples of risk mitigation (methods of solution)

| ISSUE / ACTION | Excavation in marshland |
|---|---|
| **Avoidance** Design to avoid identified hazards but beware of introducing others | No excavation would be required for a structure designed to be fabricated off-site and then ballasted to "float" at the required level. |
| **Reduction** Design to reduce identified hazards but beware of increasing others | The use of prefabricated tanks as the base units for all the large structures of the development would reduce excavation to the link buildings/corridors. |
| **Control** Design to provide acceptable safeguards for all remaining identified hazards | Design a cofferdam for the excavation of material from within. The internal water level would be controlled by pumping and the cofferdam could be incorporated into the permanent works. |

## Examples of risk mitigation (issues addressed at different stages)

A small road bridge is required across a shallow but navigable canal used by narrow boats. A lock is immediately downstream. The towpath is in constant use.

| Concept design | Scheme design | Detail design |
|---|---|---|
| Review the options for a pre-fabricated/pre-cast bridge or components to minimise the work on site. | Match the size and weight of precast components to a practicable size and location of mobile crane. | Design piles which can be installed by piling plant without intruding into the towpath and footway access. Allow space for safe delivery and stockpile of materials. |

A new suspension bridge is to cross a wide river. The steel prefabricated hollow section deck is to carry a six-lane highway. Water clearance is 30 m. A suitable road lighting system is to be provided.

| Concept design | Scheme design | Detail design |
|---|---|---|
| Appropriate illumination could be provided from edge of deck or centrally. Coordinate spacing of lights with cables and hangers and consider access for future maintenance. | Consider "drop down" columns for easier maintenance, and a permanent barrier protected corridor which accesses every lamp post. | Make the whole lamp post, lamp unit, and wiring by off-site fabrication, so that only deck level connections are necessary on site. |

GENERAL PLANNING **A**

EXCAVATIONS AND FOUNDATIONS **B**

PRIMARY STRUCTURE **C**

BUILDING ELEMENTS AND BUILDING SERVICES **D**

CIVIL ENGINEERING **E 6**

## Related issues

References within this document

| References | Related issues |
|---|---|
| A3 | Access/egress routes for materials delivery and waste disposal will be determined by local conditions. |
| A4 | Ground investigation will identify ground water levels and water quality. |
| A5 | Site layout will be determined by project under construction in relation to space available (water authority may have specific site rules). |
| B1-B7 | Excavation, drainage effects and support solutions could be crucial. Dewatering/exclusion of water will be important considerations. |
| C1-C8 | Construction components and materials may require special routes within the site and storage may also be a problem. |
| D8 | Electrical services mean electrocution is a major hazard when working near water. |
| E9 | Related issues arise |

## References for further guidance

Primary general references and background information given in Section 4

### Primary

- Construction Industry Training Board (CITB), Construction site safety notes No.30 GE 700/30 Working over water
- Building Employers Confederation (BEC), Construction safety, Section 8E Working over water 1988
- CIRIA SP137 (1997) Site safety for the water industry
- Morris, M and Simm, J (2000) Construction risk in river and estuary engineering, A guidance manual (Thomas Telford)

### Secondary

- CIRIA SP57 (1998) Handling of materials on site

### Background

- BS EN 1263-1: 1997 Safety nets. Safety requirements, test methods

### Classification

**CI/SfB**   Code (--)13

Read the Introduction before using the following guidelines

## Scope

- Cofferdams (in water, near water, in saturated ground).

## Exclusions

- Cofferdams in off-shore environments (generally subject to extensive wave pressures and aggressive climate).
- Pressurised working.

## Major hazards

Refer to the Introduction for details of accident types and health risks

**Crushed/trapped**
Collisions between boats, pontoons, crane barges, and cofferdam.
Moving plant and slewed equipment in confined space.

**Falls**
From dam wall into excavation or into water.

**Inundation**
Failure of cofferdam walls (due to water pressure/
scour/impact). Base failure (piping/heave).

**Water**
Cold water shock.
Tidal movements.
Currents and scour.
Drowning.

**Health hazards**
Contaminated ground water. Weil's Disease. Noxious gases in confined spaces. Noise and vibration from piling.

**Services**
Cables in river-bed. Temporary power cables in water. Fuel lines and storage.

## E7 Group E – Civil engineering
## 7 – Cofferdams

**A** GENERAL PLANNING

**B** EXCAVATIONS AND FOUNDATIONS

**C** PRIMARY STRUCTURE

**D** BUILDING ELEMENTS AND BUILDING SERVICES

**E 7** CIVIL ENGINEERING

### Specific hazard identification

**Possible key considerations:**

- **Project** - Can the cofferdam be wholly incorporated into the permanent structure?
- **Site investigation** - What is water table variation and extent of ground contamination? What is the underwater topography? Are there any obstructions?
- **Access** - What constraints affect movement of personnel, plant and machinery and materials delivery?
- **Adjacent water** - Is water running/still, navigable, liable to level variation, tidal, marine?
- **Environment** -What adjacent features/structures may be affected?
- **Working height** - Minimised by prefabrication of cofferdam?
- **Removal** - Will the permanent works obstruct the removal of temporary cofferdams?
- **Any others?**

### Prompts

- Project programmes
- Ground conditions
- Water levels/depths
- Contaminants/health
- Illumination
- Weather conditions
- Emergency escape routes
- Safe access
- Services
- Removal/reinstatement
- Maintenance

### Hazards consideration in design

| Stage | Considerations and issues | Possible design options to avoid or mitigate hazards identified for cofferdams |
|---|---|---|
| Concept design | | • Impact by water traffic and floating debris may be resisted by the cofferdam or separate outer defences.<br>• Consider the wider value of a temporary causeway instead of floating rigs.<br>• Prefabricated caissons towed into place are quieter and involve less work in the water than driven piled cofferdams. |
| Scheme design | • Why the cofferdam?<br>• Underwater survey<br>• Adjacent water feature<br>• Access<br>• Environment<br>• Ground investigation<br>• Contamination<br>• Programme of works<br>• Working height<br>• Support system<br>• Stability<br>• Services<br>• Noise | • Check the working platform/causeway level with respect to high tide/flood records and the intended season of works.<br>• Provide scope for structural enhancement to respond to adverse monitoring reports.<br>• Design plan shape of cofferdam to suit working space and construction plant as well as final structure. |
| Detail design | | • Design out the need for underwater working by using a different construction or remotely controlled techniques.<br>• Design in features for safe access, (eg holes and lugs for quick and easy fixing of equipment).<br>• Coordinate the design of in-situ walings with permanent structure to minimise the extent of breaking out. |

## Examples of risk mitigation (methods of solution)

| ACTION | ISSUE |
|---|---|
| | **Floating cranage and piling plant** |
| **Avoidance**<br>Design to avoid identified hazards but beware of introducing others | The use of heavy floating plant could be avoided by building the cofferdam off-site on land or in a dry dock. Instead, tug-boats would manoeuvre the floating cofferdam into position for sinking into place. |
| **Reduction**<br>Design to reduce identified hazards but beware of increasing others | For a multi-span bridge over water, the sites of foundations in shallower waters could be accessed by building a temporary causeway for land-based plant to construct the cofferdams. |
| **Control**<br>Design to provide acceptable safeguards for all remaining identified hazards | The project planning and contract periods are based on the assumption that the use of floating plant is only practicable at the turn of the tide and in good weather. |

## Examples of risk mitigation (issues addressed at different stages)

A large cofferdam is required for a bridge foundation in a river.

| Concept design | Scheme design | Detail design |
|---|---|---|
| Consider permanent structure to be constructed. Consider effects on local marine movements to determine working space available. | Assume space available for double skin earth filled parallel walls. Provides safer working area, no internal strutting. | Wall design, drainage design, need for cross walls, include flexible and convenient details for the addition of working platforms. |

A warehouse with deep basement storage is to be constructed adjacent to a navigable river - excavation for the foundation of the building is in saturated alluvial material.

| Concept design | Scheme design | Detail design |
|---|---|---|
| Consider adjacent structures and environment to determine appropriate cofferdam type. Assume an external support. | Multi-level ground anchors or raking piles (instead of walings) provide safer working areas by being less intrusive into the confined space. | Consider the stability of adjacent structures and river bank, and review options for ground works in the intervening space to minimise their risk exposure. Include ground water and earth pressure monitoring devices to guide future maintenance/remedial work. |

GENERAL PLANNING — A

EXCAVATIONS AND FOUNDATIONS — B

PRIMARY STRUCTURE — C

BUILDING ELEMENTS AND BUILDING SERVICES — D

CIVIL ENGINEERING — E7

**A** GENERAL PLANNING

**B** EXCAVATIONS AND FOUNDATIONS

**C** PRIMARY STRUCTURE

**D** BUILDING ELEMENTS AND BUILDING SERVICES

**E7** CIVIL ENGINEERING

## Related issues

References within this document

| References | Related issues |
|---|---|
| A1,B6 | Local environment is affected by piling which gives rise to noise and vibration. The effects on local buildings, industry and the general public must be considered. |
| A3 | Access/egress routes for materials delivery and waste removal may also be dictated by local environment. |
| A4 | Ground investigation is an important consideration in choice of support system. |
| B1,B2 | Excavations inside cofferdams mean crucial considerations include ground conditions, drainage effects, support solutions and dewatering. |
| C1-C8 | Foundations and Primary Structure may be constructed inside cofferdams. |
| D8 | Electrical services mean electrocution is a major hazard when working near water. |
| E6 | Working near water will involve additional hazards. |

## References for further guidance

Primary general references and background information given in Section 4

### Primary

- CIRIA SP95 The design and construction of sheet piled cofferdams 1993

### Secondary

- CIRIA SP57 (1988) Handling of materials on site
- Tomlinson, M J (2001) Foundation design and construction. 7th ed (Prentice Hall)

### Background

- Arcelor (2005) Piling handbook. 8th ed

### Classification

**CI/SfB**   Code (--)187

Read the Introduction before using the following guidelines

## Scope

- Pipes: carrying water, sewage, gas, oil, etc. or used as protection for cables and "piped" services.
- Cables: for power, telephone, TV, other communications cables.

## Exclusions

- Power cables for railways.
- Trenches (see B3).

## Major hazards

Refer to the Introduction for details of accident types and health risks

**Falls**
From construction and maintenance plant and equipment.
Into trenches and excavations.

**Buried/crushed/trapped**
Struck by plant and machinery.
Collapse of trench or excavation.

**Services**
Power – electrocution.
Gas and fuel – explosions.
Sewers – health hazards and sharps.

**Health hazards**
Contaminated ground and water (eg Weil's Disease).
Sewage and other effluents.
Noise.
Dust.

**Asphyxiation**
Working in confined spaces and access chambers.
Harmful gases.

**Traffic**
Cabling over roads/railways.
Runaway vehicles entering area of work.
Access chambers in the highway.

## Specific hazard identification

**Possible key considerations:**

- **Facility** - What type of pipe or wire? What is it conveying?
- **Site survey** - What are site conditions? What other services are present (overhead or underground)? How high, how deep are they? What ground contaminants are present?
- **Working room** - Is there sufficient space for plant and machinery?
- **Environment** - Is work next to structures, buildings, road, railway, also near to water? Special procedures? Need for double protection for containment?
- **Access:** What site access route problems exist? Is there room to work on new systems installation?
- **Interface** - With utilities and services to buildings/structures.
- **Any others?**

## Prompts

- Ground conditions
- What service?
- Contamination
- Access
- Possession
- Maintenance
- Confined spaces (access chambers)
- Party wall interfaces
- Existing systems
- Trace heating
- Lagging
- Access for maintenance
- Provision for future adaptation

## Hazards consideration in design

| Stage | Considerations and issues | Possible design options to avoid or mitigate hazards identified for pipes and cables |
|---|---|---|
| Concept design | • Site location<br>• Existing information<br>• Access<br>• Possession<br>• Type of pipe/cable<br>• Height and depth<br>• Services | • Review current data to determine the benefit of tracing or surveying some of the existing services.<br>• Review the possibility of co-ordinating the work with planned work by other utilities to streamline construction operations and reduce public disruption.<br>• Investigate existing services fully.<br>• Concept design to minimise need for access into chambers etc for cleaning. |
| Scheme design | • Ground conditions<br>• Adjacent features<br>• Sequence<br>• Working space<br>• Maintenance<br>• Local environment (type of conduit/<br>temperature control)<br>• Other services | • Plan the route to avoid existing services and minimise the likelihood of disturbance by other construction activity.<br>• Ensure that the design provides for easy location and access to make future connections.<br>• Provide ventilation of enclosed spaces.<br>• Arrange layout to assist access to valves.<br>• Provide permanent access and use during construction. |
| Detail design | • Cleaning and access requirements<br>• Build-up of gases<br>• Access for CCTV<br>• Exclusion of public<br>• Permanent access | • Whenever possible choose details which anticipate technical change.<br>• Balance the provision of convenient, safe access for future maintenance against easy access by untrained or unauthorised persons.<br>• Provide double-valve isolation for man access.<br>• Use V-J-type couplings to assist future work.<br>• Provide overhead lifting systems for heavy pipes and equipment. |

## Examples of risk mitigation (methods of solution)

| ACTION / ISSUE | In-trench jointing of pipes | Crossing a major road |
|---|---|---|
| **Avoidance**<br>Design to avoid identified hazards but beware of introducing others | Select a pipe/duct capable of being laid from a "reel" located above ground. | Route the service over an existing bridge or micro-bore under the road. |
| **Reduction**<br>Design to reduce identified hazards but beware of increasing others | Choose quick and simple jointing (eg push-fit or hinged clamps instead of lead filled or welded connections). | Connect excavations on each side of the carriageway by pipe-jacking a service duct between them. |
| **Control**<br>Design to provide acceptable safeguards for all remaining identified hazards | Locate complicated joints where wider excavation is possible and likely. | Design for construction in short lengths to suit an acceptable sequence of lane closures. |

## Examples of risk mitigation (issues addressed at different stages)

A new sewer is to be laid in an urban environment. Records have identified underground power cables which cross the alignment and sometimes run parallel to the alignment.

| Concept design | Scheme design | Detail design |
|---|---|---|
| Re-examine route of sewer to avoid underground services. | Prove information by trial pits and electro-magnetic tracing. Determine the width of working corridor required. Consider use of trenchless techniques.<br><br>Route cannot be changed. | Trenchless techniques chosen. Specify location of access pits and alignment of sewer to avoid existing services. |

To release development land an underground network of pipes for power station cooling water has to be partially replaced and diverted.

| Concept design | Scheme design | Detail design |
|---|---|---|
| Consider the future maintenance benefit of a whole new network. Review alternative routes and combinations of overhead and underground alignments. | Favour options which allow complete construction of the new routes before breaking into the existing network. | Maintain access to live services during construction. Define the working zone to minimise overlap between construction activities and the operation of the power station. |

Side tabs:
- A GENERAL PLANNING
- B EXCAVATIONS AND FOUNDATIONS
- C PRIMARY STRUCTURE
- D BUILDING ELEMENTS AND BUILDING SERVICES
- E8 CIVIL ENGINEERING

## Related issues

References within this document

| References | Related issues |
|---|---|
| A1 | Surrounding environment will be affected by pipe and cable work (including maintenance operations). |
| A2 | Demolition of a structure must include identification and marking of services that are isolated or redundant. The Health and safety file should be available. |
| A4 | Access/egress routes and facilities for maintenance should be free from obstruction. |
| B3 | Trench excavations must be suitably supported. |
| D8 | Electrical services. |
| E2 | Working space for pipes and cables are invariably adjacent to or under roadways. When traffic measures are required during construction or maintenance, consider space and barriers to protect site personnel. |

## References for further guidance

Primary general references and background information given in Section 4

### Primary

- HSE HSG47 Avoiding danger from underground services
- HSE GS6 Avoidance of danger from overhead electric power lines
- HSE CIS8 (revised) Safety in excavations
- CIRIA SP57 Handling of materials on site 1988

### Secondary

- CIRIA R97 Trenching practice 1992
- CIRIA TN127 Trenchless construction for underground services 1987
- HSE MDHS100 Surveying sampling and assessment of asbestos coating materials

### Background

- DfT (2006) Traffic Signs Manual chapter 8: roadworks and temporary situations. 2 parts
- HSE INDG84L – Leptospirosis: are you at risk?
- Pipeline Industries Guild (1994) Pipelines: all you wanted to know… but were afraid to ask
- Hughes, H (1997) Telecommunications cables: manufacture and installation (John Wiley)

### Classification

**CI/SfB**    Code (--)I/J

Read the Introduction before using the following guidelines

## Scope

- Exposed Tidal waters (eg Coastal waters, harbours, estuaries) where wave, wind and currents impact on the construction methodology, plant band environment.

GENERAL PLANNING **A**

EXCAVATIONS AND FOUNDATIONS **B**

PRIMARY STRUCTURE **C**

BUILDING ELEMENTS AND BUILDING SERVICES **D**

CIVIL ENGINEERING **E 9**

## Exclusions

- Working over/near water (See E6)

## Major hazards

Refer to the Introduction for details of accident types and health risks

**Slips, trips and falls** due to:
Wet, algae-covered surfaces.
Awkward access.
Unstable and moving platforms.
Moving water.
Exposed locations.

**Crushed/trapped** due to:
Moving plant.
Inter-vessel personnel transfer.
Impact by boats and pontoons.
Struck by plant or slewed materials and equipment.

**Health hazards** due to:
Lack of accessible welfare provisions due to exposed/remote location
Contaminated water:
– Water-borne diseases (eg Weill's Disease).
– Chemicals contamination

**Immersion**
Cold water shock
Hypothermia
Fatigue
Drowning

**Moving water**
River currents, scour
Tidal movements.
Flood water

**Unsafe temporary structures**
Unconsolidated seabed material.
Seabed changes
Temporary storage eg rock dump

**A** GENERAL PLANNING

**B** EXCAVATIONS AND FOUNDATIONS

**C** PRIMARY STRUCTURE

**D** BUILDING ELEMENTS AND BUILDING SERVICES

**E 9** CIVIL ENGINEERING

## Specific hazard identification

**Possible key considerations:**

- **Don't ignore the normal hazards** (eg slips trips and falls) but consider how the environment might affect them
- **Site data/location:**
  - What are tidal and surge conditions?
  - What are the wave conditions?
  - What are the flow conditions?
  - What are the possible changes in ground/seabed level and condition?
- **Access/egress** – What is required/practicable to make safe? What are the methods for transferring personnel to vessels?
- **Working room** – What plant will be used? Where will plant and materials be located?
- **Working level** – What are the methods to safeguard falling from height? What measures are in place to recover personnel (including suspension after falls)?
- **The public** – how will the public be excluded from working/unsafe areas?
- **Any others?**

## Prompts

- Guard rails/barriers
- Protection of public
- Contamination
- Illumination
- Weather conditions
- Seasonal changes
- Ground conditions
- Welfare facilities

## Hazards consideration in design

| Stage | Considerations and issues | Possible design options to avoid or mitigate hazards identified for deep basements and shafts |
|---|---|---|
| Concept design | | • Choose a prefabricated construction to avoid/minimise fabrication over water.<br>• Divert or exclude the water by dams and pumping.<br>• Consider cofferdams to exclude or isolate the water hazards.<br>• Check whether working space or bed conditions exclude any construction methods. |
| Scheme design | • Site survey<br>• Water type/depth<br>• Location<br>• Services<br>• Geotechnical investigation<br>• Working space<br>• Contamination<br>• Safe access<br>• Advance works (services, drainage)<br>• Excavations<br>• Emergency procedures<br>• Sequence of operations | • Ascertain a programme and design for the works to be carried out at low tide only.<br>• Maximise the types of component which could be prefabricated.<br>• Examine sequences of working to minimise period of exposure. |
| Detail design | | • Select more durable materials and finishes for surfaces which require maintenance access over water (i.e. fewer visits required).<br>• New works to include provision for future maintenance: safe removable access where possible.<br>• Remove/reduce underwater fixings to avoid diver-placement |

## Examples of risk mitigation (methods of solution)

**ISSUE**

**ACTION**

| | **Constructing under water formations** |
|---|---|
| **Avoidance**<br>Design to avoid identified hazards but beware of introducing others | No excavation would be required for a structure designed to be fabricated off-site and then ballasted to "float" at the required level. |
| **Reduction**<br>Design to reduce identified hazards but beware of increasing others | The use of prefabricated tanks as the base units for all the large structures of the development would reduce excavation to the link buildings/corridors |
| **Control**<br>Design to provide acceptable safeguards for all remaining identified hazards | Design a cofferdam for the excavation of material from within. The internal water level would be controlled by pumping and the cofferdam could be incorporated into the permanent works. |

## Examples of risk mitigation (issues addressed at different stages)

An old Victorian pier is being refurbished in a busy seaside resort.

| **Concept design** | **Scheme design** | **Detail design** |
|---|---|---|
| Review the options for a pre-fabricated/pre-cast solution or components to minimise the work on site. | Minimise the number of precast components whilst using a practicable crane size.<br><br>Allow space for safe delivery and stockpile of materials.<br><br>Remove underwater fixings where possible to avoid diver working. | Allow removal of existing fittings for repair in workshop environment rather than repair over water.<br><br>Provide access/fixing points for ease of maintenance/painting. |

A costal protection scheme is required to protect an urban area involving beach recharge and groynes

| **Concept design** | **Scheme design** | **Detail design** |
|---|---|---|
| Risk assessment to compare:<br>• Placement of sand recharge<br>• Repairing groins in tidal areas<br>• Offshore breakwater | Required placing methodology to avoid soft ground areas which may be hazardous to public. | Consider using standard timber details rather than varying details to limit amount of cutting work required. |

GENERAL PLANNING **A**

EXCAVATIONS AND FOUNDATIONS **B**

PRIMARY STRUCTURE **C**

BUILDING ELEMENTS AND BUILDING SERVICES **D**

CIVIL ENGINEERING **E 9**

**A** GENERAL PLANNING

**B** EXCAVATIONS AND FOUNDATIONS

**C** PRIMARY STRUCTURE

**D** BUILDING ELEMENTS AND BUILDING SERVICES

**E 9** CIVIL ENGINEERING

## Related issues

References within this document

| References | Related issues |
|---|---|
| A4 | Ground investigation will identify ground water levels and water quality. |
| A3 | Access/egress routes for materials delivery and waste disposal will be determined by local conditions. |
| A5 | Site layout will be determined by project under construction in relation to space available (water authority may have specific site rules). |
| B1–B7 | Excavation, drainage effects and support solutions could be crucial. Dewatering/exclusion of water will be important considerations. |
| C1–C8 | Construction components and materials may require special routes within the site and storage may also be a problem. |
| D8 | Electrical services mean electrocution is a major hazard when working near water. |
| E6 | Related issues arise. |

## References for further guidance

Primary general references and background information given in Section 4

### Primary

- Construction Industry Training Board, Construction site safety notes No.30 GE 700//30 Working over water (1992)
- Building Employers Confederation, Construction safety, Section 8E Working over water (1988)
- Morris, M and Simm, J (2000) Construction risk in river and estuary engineering, A guidance manual (Thomas Telford)
- CIRIA C518 Safety in ports, ship-to-shore linkspans and walkways
- Moth, P (1998) Work boat code of practice – an operational guide (Forecourt Publications)

### Secondary

- CIRIA SP130 (1997) Site safety for the water industry
- CIRIA R158 (1996) Sea outfalls – inspection and diver safety
- CIRIA R159 (1996) Sea outfalls – construction inspection and repair. An engineering guide
- HSE HSG177 Managing health and safety in dockwork

### Background

- CIRIA C584 Coastal and marine environmental site guide (2003)
- Cork R S, Cruickshank I C (2005) Construction safety in coastal and maritime engineering (Thomas Telford)

### Classification

CAWS    Group A,    CEWS    Class T,

# 3 Providing information

## THE PROVISION AND USE OF HEALTH AND SAFETY INFORMATION

This chapter provides additional guidance in support of the information in Section 1.4.8.

Designers have a duty to provide information on the significant risks in the design that cannot be avoided (see 3.2 below). In addition, designers may wish to document the health and safety considerations made during the design to:

- ❑ keep track of hazards that have not yet been resolved
- ❑ indicate the range of design options that were considered at any stage
- ❑ communicate information to the CDM coordinator and other designers.

Documents should not be allowed to create a significant burden of extra paperwork; the ACoP emphasises throughout that paperwork must not be for its own sake and that bureaucracy must be minimised. Paperwork should be used only as an aid to thinking, communication and recording what has been done and as an aid to any audits or investigations that may occur. Many organisations already use management systems such as quality assurance; recording the consideration of health and safety during design will form one part of any such system.

The provision by designers of drawings and specifications is normal. Additionally, other statements or special reports or both may be needed when:

- ❑ the work to be done poses potential risks to people in adjacent structures
- ❑ the work to be done poses potential risks to the public or the client's own employees or customers
- ❑ the structure is of a nature that might pose health and safety risks to competent contractors (for example, having an unusual structure or one which is prone to instability during erection)
- ❑ designers have made assumptions about the likely method of work and sequence of construction that contractors will need to know in order to assess what needs to be done and to devise safe working methods; the provision of a method statement may be a useful way to communicate the hazards to contractors.

A designer will need to understand how each structure can be constructed or assembled safely. When a designer does not have the required specialist knowledge, it will be necessary to consult with the CDM coordinator or with specialists. Recognition of one's own limits and arranging access to specialist advice is part of a designer's competence.

Information about the design will be communicated in various forms including:

- drawings
- outline method statements
- specifications/scope of works
- special report(s).

These can be included as tender documentation. However, it should normally be made clear that the information does not preclude a contractor's consideration of other options. Designers should provide relevant information and then cooperate with contractors. Contractors may consult designers, but will be responsible for their construction methods as they develop.

Exceptions to the above might include circumstances where it is intended to impose a particular method of construction on a contractor, eg when designers have assumed a particular sequence of erection to prevent buckling of the partially complete structure or when a safe method of working has already been approved by a responsible body. In such cases procurement documents should require contractors to confirm that the proposed method(s) are acceptable and they are able to manage them safely on site. These issues should be clear within the pre-construction information. The competence and resources to manage the residual risk will be key factors influencing the selection of any contractor involved in this aspect of the project.

## 3.2    INFORMATION FOR IN-HOUSE RECORDS

Designers may like to keep their own records of the hazards they have identified and how they have dealt with the associated risks. These will be discussed during design reviews and progress meetings and the appropriate records should form part of the normal system for project management. There will be practical reasons to keep records, in case of personnel changes, unexpected delays in the progress of the design, or in the case of future dispute. This guidance does not prescribe how designers should record their considerations and decisions arising from compliance with the CDM Regulations, as each practice will have its own approach when establishing procedures and audit trails.

Designers may find it helpful to develop standard forms for recording the health and safety decisions for their projects. This may include the actions they have been able to take to eliminate hazards and reduce risks. Such forms may also include a consideration by the designer of whether the residual risk is sufficiently significant or unusual to be outside the scope of a competent contractor in the context of the project, and therefore a candidate for inclusion in the pre-construction information and/or file.

However, note that the HSE have repeatedly explained that one of the drivers for CDM2007 was to try to stop the practice of preparing and passing to others large amounts of documentation of minimal use. **All documentation created should focus upon important hazards on the project in hand and be an aid to effective communication.**

# 4    Sources of further information

The references given below and in each of the work sectors in Chapter 2 were correct at the date of publication. However, reference documents are liable to be updated, superseded or withdrawn and readers are urged to check that they have obtained the most up-to-date references. See also further references in the ACoP.

## Publications

**HEALTH AND SAFETY COMMISSION**
*Managing Health and Safety in Construction: Construction (Design and Management) Regulations 2007*

Approved Code of Practice  L144
HSE Books 2007

*Health and Safety in Construction HSG 150*
HSE Books 2006

*Protecting the public: your next move HSG151*
HSE Books 1997

*Construction Information Sheets (CIS series) – various topics*
HSE Books

*Dust and noise in the construction process*
*Ferguson I. Contract Research Report 73*
HSE Books 1995

*Provision of welfare facilities at fixed construction sites CIS18*
HSE Books 2004

*Fire safety in construction work HSG 168*
HSE Books 1997

*Harness suspension: review and evaluation of existing information  RR451*
HSE Books 2002

*A technical guide to the selection and use of fall prevention and arrest equipment RR302*
HSE Books 2005

*Improving the safety of workers in the vicinity of mobile plant  RR358*
HSE Books 2001

*Preventing falls from boom-type mobile elevating working platforms  Misc 614*
*HSE Information Sheet*

**THE CONSTRUCTION CONFEDERATION**
*Construction Safety*
Construction Industry Publications Ltd (frequently updated).

**CONSTRUCTION INDUSTRY TRAINING BOARD (CITB)**
*Construction Site Safety – Health Safety and Environment*
Safety Notes GE700 (frequently updated, being updated for CDM2007)
Published by CITB

**DAVIES V J AND TOMASIN K**
*Construction Safety Handbook*
Thomas Telford 1996

**CIRIA**

*Site safety: a handbook for young construction professionals (3rd edition)*
CIRIA Special Publication 151, 2001

*Handling of materials on site, Publication SP57*
CIRIA 1988

*Crane stability on site: an introductory guide, Publication SP131*
CIRIA 1996

*Temporary access to the workface: a handbook for young professionals, Publication SP121*
CIRIA 1995

*Access for maintenance and repair: Design guidance, Publication C611*
CIRIA 2004

*A guide to the Control of Substances Hazardous to Health in design and construction, Publication R125*
CIRIA 1993

*Operating and maintenance manuals for buildings, a guide to procurement and preparation, Publication C507*
CIRIA 1999

*Remedial processes for contaminated land – principles and practices, Publication C549*
CIRIA 2001

*Contaminated land risk assessment – a guide to good practice, Publication C552*
CIRIA 2001

*Faster construction on site by selection of methods and materials, Publication C560*
CIRIA 2001

*Integrating safety, quality and environmental management, Publication C509*
CIRIA 2000

*Facilities management manuals – a best practice guide, Publication C581*
CIRIA 2002

*Design for deconstruction; Publication C607*
CIRIA 2004

*Site health handbook; Publication C629*
CIRIA 2004

*CDM2007 – Workplace 'in-use' guidance for designers, Publication C663*
CIRIA 2007

**British Standards**
BS 7121 (various parts) *Code of practice for safe use of cranes*

BS 7212:2006 *Code of practice for the safe use of construction hoists*

BS 8093:1991 *Code of Practice for the use of safety nets, containment nets and sheets on construction work*

BS 8437:2006 *Code of practice for selection, use and maintenance of personal fall protection systems and equipment for use in the workplace*

**Websites**

www.citb-constructionskills.co.uk/CDM
Industry guidance

www.hse.gov.uk
The HSE website – see the Construction Industry area

www.hsebooks.co.uk
Search for publications

www.safetyindesign.org
Industry guidance

www.dbp.org.uk
Case studies

www.scoss.org.uk
SCOSS website

# Appendix A    Checklist of hazard management

NOTE: This checklist contains generic information. It is indicative, not exhaustive and must be used only to facilitate careful consideration of the specific hazards discussed and levels of risk on a specific project; see also Chapter 2 for guidance.

<table>
<tr><td colspan="3">CDM – Hazard management checklist</td></tr>
<tr><td colspan="2" align="center">Issue</td><td align="center">Response</td></tr>
<tr><td>a)</td><td>Select the position and design of structures to minimise risks from site hazards, including:<br><br>– buried services, including gas pipelines<br>– overhead cables<br>– traffic movements to, from and around the site<br>– contaminated ground, for example minimising disturbance by using shallow excavations and driven, rather than bored, piles.</td><td></td></tr>
<tr><td>b)</td><td>Design out health hazards, for example:<br><br>– specify less hazardous materials eg solvent-free or low solvent adhesives and water-based paints<br>– avoid processes that create hazardous fumes, vapours, dust, noise or vibration, including disturbance of existing asbestos, cutting chases in brickwork and concrete, breaking down cast in-situ piles to level, scabbling concrete, hand digging tunnels, flame cutting or sanding areas coated with lead paint or cadmium<br>– specify materials that are easy to handle, eg lighter weight building blocks<br>– design block paved areas to enable mechanical handling and laying of blocks.</td><td></td></tr>
<tr><td>c)</td><td>Design out safety hazards, for example:<br><br>– the need for work at height, particularly where it would involve work from ladders, or where safe means of access and a safe place of work is not provided<br>– fragile roofing materials<br>– deep or long excavations in public areas or on highways<br>– materials that could create a significant fire risk during construction.</td><td></td></tr>
<tr><td>d)</td><td>Consider prefabrication to minimise hazardous work or to allow it to be carried out in more controlled conditions off-site including for example:<br><br>– design elements, such as structural steel work and process plant, so that sub-assemblies can be erected at ground level and then safely lifted into place<br>– arrange for cutting to size to be done off-site, under controlled conditions, to reduce the amount of dust release.</td><td></td></tr>
<tr><td>e)</td><td>Design in features that reduce the risk of falling/injury where it is not possible to avoid work at height, for example:<br><br>– early installation of permanent access, such as stairs, to reduce the use of ladders<br>– edge protection or other features that increase the safety of access and construction.</td><td></td></tr>
</table>

CIRIA C662                                           193                    CDM2007 Construction work sector guidance for designers

| CDM – Hazard management checklist (continued) | |
|---|---|
| **Issue** | **Response** |
| f)   Design to simplify safe construction, for example:<br><br>   – provide lifting points and mark the weight, and centre of gravity of heavy or awkward items requiring slinging both on drawings and on the items themselves<br><br>   – make allowance for temporary works required during construction<br><br>   – design joints in vertical structural steel members so that bolting up can easily be done by someone standing on a permanent floor, and by use of seating angles to provide support while the bolts are put in place<br><br>   – design connections to minimise the risk of incorrect assembly. | |
| g)   Design to simplify future maintenance and cleaning work, for example:<br>   – make provision for safe permanent access<br>   – specify windows that can be cleaned from the inside<br>   – design plant rooms to allow safe access to plant and for its removal and replacement<br>   – design safe access for roof-mounted plant, and roof maintenance<br>   – make provision for safe temporary access to allow for painting and maintenance of facades etc. This might involve allowing for access by mobile elevating work platforms or for erection of scaffolding. | |
| h)   Identify demolition hazards for inclusion in the health and safety file, for example:<br>   – sources of substantial stored energy, including pre- or post-tensioned members<br>   – unusual stability concepts<br>   – alterations that have changed the structure. | |
| i)   Understand how the structure can be constructed, cleaned and maintained safely:<br><br>   – taking full account of the risks that can arise during the proposed construction processes, giving particular attention to new or unfamiliar processes, and to those that may place large numbers of people at risk<br><br>   – considering the stability of partially erected structures and, where necessary, providing information to show how temporary stability could be achieved during construction<br><br>   – considering the effect of proposed work on the integrity of existing structures, particularly during refurbishment<br><br>   – ensuring that the overall design takes full account of any temporary works, for example falsework, which may be needed, no matter who is to develop those works<br><br>   – ensuring that there are suitable arrangements (for example access and hard standing) for cranes, and other heavy equipment, if required. | |
| j)   Anything else? | |

# Appendix B    Checklist of information to be provided

NOTE: This checklist contains generic information. It is indicative, not exhaustive and must be used only to facilitate careful consideration of the specific hazards and levels of risk on a specific project; see also Chapter 2 for guidance.

| CDM – Information checklist | |
|---|---|
| **Issue** | **Response** |
| a) | Designers must include adequate health and safety information with the design. This includes information about significant hazards that remain in the design, and the resulting risks – see (b) below. They need to make clear any assumptions about working methods or precautions, so that the people carrying out the construction work can take them into account. | |
| b) | Designers do not need to mention every hazard or assumption, as this can obscure the significant issues, but they do need to point out significant hazards. These are not necessarily those that result in the greatest risks, but those that are: <br><br> – not likely to be obvious to a competent contractor or other designers <br><br> – unusual, or <br><br> – likely to be difficult to manage effectively. <br><br> To identify significant hazards designers must understand how the design can be built. | |
| c) | Examples of significant hazards where designers always need to provide information include: <br><br> – hazards that could cause multiple fatalities to the public, such as tunnelling, or the use of a crane close to a busy public place, major road or railway <br><br> – temporary works, required to ensure stability during the construction, alteration or demolition of the whole or any part of the structure, eg bracing during construction of steel or concrete frame buildings <br><br> – hazardous or flammable substances specified in the design, eg epoxy grouts, fungicidal paints, or those containing isocyanates <br><br> – features of the design and sequences of assembly or disassembly that are crucial to safe working <br><br> – specific problems and possible solutions for example arrangements to enable the removal of a large item of plant from the basement of a building <br><br> – structures that create particular access problems, such as domed glass structures <br><br> – heavy or awkward prefabricated elements likely to create risks in handling <br><br> – areas needing access where normal methods of tying scaffolds may not be feasible, such as facades that have no opening windows and cannot be drilled. | |

| CDM – Information checklist (continued) | |
|---|---|
| **Issue** | **Response** |
| d) Information should be clear, precise, and in a form suitable for the users. This can be achieved using, for example:<br><br>   — notes on drawings – these are immediately available to those carrying out the work, they can refer to other documents if more detail is needed, and be annotated to keep them up to date<br><br>   — a register, or lists of significant residual hazards<br><br>   — suggested construction sequence showing how the design could be erected safely, where this is not obvious, for example suggested sequences for putting up stressed skin roofs. Contractors may then adopt this method or develop their own approach. | |
| e) Anything else? | |

# Appendix C

## EXAMPLES OF HAZARD ELIMINATION AND RISK REDUCTION BY DESIGNERS.

Two examples are provided. The first example shows the team thinking at an early stage of consideration of planning for the refurbishment of an underground station. Here the discussion is necessarily quite "broad-brush" but health and safety matters are being considered as an integral part of the planning/design process.

The second example shows the team thinking at a more advanced stage of design for a block of offices. Earlier discussions had identified issues to do with the roof as being of concern; the team considered various options for the roofscape and this example records the decisions made.

**Example 1: An underground station is to be refurbished.**

The requirement is to keep the station open for as long as is reasonably practicable; weekend closures are less disruptive than weekday closures and a closure over a long weekend at Easter may be agreed (but this is unlikely). The station is not as busy as most, but it is used steadily throughout the day and evening. The members of the design team have considered the need and are meeting to discuss what solutions will be developed. At the meeting, the CDM issues are addressed using Appendices A and B, adapted to suit the work under consideration.

# Hazard Elimination and Risk Reduction

| Issue | Response |
|---|---|
| Select the position and design of structures to minimise risks from site hazards. *In this case the site cannot be selected; however, the works may be designed in different ways and the options need to be considered.* | The key site hazards are identified as:<br><br>1　Working in areas used by other contractors/client staff/company staff.<br>2　Working in spaces used by the train operator's staff, vehicles and customers.<br>3　Working on existing fragile structures.<br>4　Protection to special Features (English Heritage).<br>5　Working in confined spaces.<br>6　Working at height in some areas.<br>7　Restricted working conditions (dust; restricted hot working).<br>8　Working under onerous time constraints (01:00 am to 04:00 am) (Unlikely to get possession, but if possession required, three months for application min).<br>9　Working in areas of restricted access (security/sensitive equipment).<br>10　Restricted loads in lifts and on escalators (manual handling/double bagging) (licenses required).<br>11　Safety in design – slip resistances, lighting, air conditioning, restricted heat emission systems, noise reduction systems and other environmental condition assessments/improvements/additions.<br>12　Working in areas with electrical circuits.<br>13　Working in areas adjacent to sensitive safety-critical signaling systems. |
| | Asbestos and other dangerous materials have already been tested for and are not present.<br><br>The design team identify the following options:<br><br>1　Use traditional methods and materials applied in work possessions/engineering hours.<br>2　Small components for easy transport/ manual handling.<br>3　Develop off-site prefabrication methods applied in work possessions or close-downs where possible (unlikely).<br>4　Use traditional "Underground Rail" methods and materials.<br><br>After discussion, it is decided that a combination of option 4 and option 2 will be pursued. For deep-level work, track-side vehicles will be used to cart away old materials at night and to deliver light-weight prefabricated panels. |

# Hazard Elimination and Risk Reduction (continued)

| Issue | Response |
|---|---|
| Design out health hazards | Much of the work will be off-site but removal of old materials and drilling for the attachment of new materials are unavoidable. Therefore, tools will be procured which have (a) in-built dust-extraction and (b) low noise and vibration output, (c) are intrinsically safe. |
| | Similarly, old materials will need to be carted away; it is envisaged that, manual handling needs to be minimized by the use of stair walkers, light-weight chutes, lift protectors and trolleys. Load route planning required. |
| | New units will need to be lifted and fixed into place; to facilitate this work it is envisaged that a small robot will need to be developed, using technology from the cladding industry. |
| | Environmental issues with "modern standards" require improvements to lighting, emergency lighting, slip resistance to flooring, contrast to signage and way finding, sound systems, air conditioning, platform safety and ambient noise levels. Addressed by the selection of suitable products and materials. |
| | Fire – products, equipment and materials must have the requisite fire protection/ fire resistance and consideration to the effects of fire must be undertaken with a view to appropriate use of fire detection, suppression and compartmentation, with fire escape plans being created for each construction phase and for the permanent condition. |
| Design out safety hazards | Even employing the ideas outlined above, the design team are concerned that operatives will be involved in accidents due to the need to complete a large amount of work in a short time, in confined areas and with other workers present carrying out other works and duties. Therefore, the designers recommend that the procurement should be designed such that good site management and control will be priced in and rewarded. |
| Consider prefabrication to minimise hazardous work or to allow it to be carried out in more controlled conditions off-site | Adopted after much debate; the decision will require development of components which meet strict fire regulations and are hard-wearing and vandal-resistant. World-wide research has fortunately shown that this can be done and technology partners are found to provide the necessary expertise. It is noted however that due to access and others working in the stations that there will be issues restricting size of such components |
| Design in features that reduce the risk of falling/injury | A rapidly installed track-side protection system is to be developed to avoid falls onto the track and also to prevent dust entering the working rail system and signaling. Also investigation into protection systems will be undertaken in respect to avoid dust entering escalator, lift, relays, cable ducts, signaling equipment and other working parts. |
| Design to simplify safe construction | The need for detailed design to facilitate fast easy assembly at site will at the same time meet this objective. All site work will need to be fully planned to the last detail. |
| | Will also need to consider varying wind pressures from trains, excessive loading conditions (cable drums on platforms/concourses/bridges) and restricted access (bends in access tunnels etc). |
| Design to simplify future maintenance and cleaning work, where there are conflicting requirements. | The detailed specification to be developed by the designers is to include:<br>1 Easy cleaning/ slip resistance floors.<br>2 The facility to easily remove and replace parts which may be damaged.<br>3 Vandal proof.<br>4 Fire proof.<br>5 Security. |
| Identify demolition hazards | It is not envisaged that the work could affect the stability of the main structure, but this possibility would have severe consequences. Therefore the designers propose that:<br>1 All removal of materials adhering to earth-retaining structure near the running tunnels should be during the nightly shut-down period.<br>2 The earth-retaining structures should be observed and their condition recorded where they are exposed.<br>3 Any matters of concern should be reported immediately and competent experts be available for consultation with emergency preparedness plans in place. |

## Provision of Information

| Issue | Response |
|---|---|
| Designers must include adequate health and safety information with the design. This includes information about hazards that remain in the design, and the resulting risks. They need to make clear any assumptions about working methods or precautions, so that the people carrying out the construction work can take them into account. | In this case, the situation is complex and the designers recommend *that they meet with the contractors, maintainers, users and other stakeholders at the earliest possible time to discuss the risks fully.* |
| To identify significant hazards designers must understand how the design can be built, maintained, used and decommissioned. | The proposed solution requires further development before its ramifications are fully clear; this is understood by the designers and they record this and agree to continue to examine CDM issues in detail at future meetings. |

**Notes to example 1:**

1   The above example shows typical output information from the discussion of a new project. It is indicative, not exhaustive and must only be used to facilitate understanding of the CDM work of a designer; see also Chapter 2 for guidance.

2   Note that "in-use" risks are considered here, as well as construction risks, as required by CDM2007. Guidance on workplace 'in-use' considerations is available in CIRIA publication C663, *CDM2007 – Workplace "in-use" guidance for designers.*

**Example 2:** **The scheme design for the roofscape of a multi-storey office block.**

The team have already identified issues arising from "at height" hazards at the planning stage.

| Hazard Elimination and Risk Reduction | |
|---|---|
| **Issue** | **Response** |
| Need for roof areas which are not protected from falling from height | The architectural concept adopted a flat roof which was in keeping with the local streetscape; in addition, a flat roof was considered to be intrinsically safer for subsequent maintenance than a pitched roof. The decision to omit a perimeter wall was made for aesthetic reasons and also because there was a strict height limit at the perimeter, such that the provision of a perimeter wall would have resulted in the loss of a full storey of accommodation. |
| Ability of people to access roof areas | The designers decided to provide access to the roof through a small penthouse structure accessed by an extension of the stairs. It was realized that this route might be used for escape in a severe fire. Access through the door onto the roof was therefore either through an alarmed fire-door or through a door which could be opened with a key held in a secure cabinet. Access was onto a secure area with a gate onto the roof which again could be opened with a key held in a secure cabinet. The secure area was considered to be large enough for those escaping a fire to congregate within, and the fire services were consulted on the escape philosophy and details. |
| Need for operatives to access open roof areas. | The roofing material selected was a long-life material which would not require regular inspection and maintenance. It was designed to drain to a gutter within the secure area, so that no maintenance outside that area was envisaged. |
| Provision for working outside the secure area. | On the basis that work outside the secure area would be rare, provision was made for attachments to be made to strong points on the structure of the perimeter of the secure area but no permanent equipment was installed. Provision was also made in the perimeter detailing for the attachment of future temporary perimeter fencing. |
| **Provision of information** | |
| Designers must include adequate health and safety information with the design. This includes information about hazards that remain in the design, and the resulting risks. They need to make clear any assumptions about working methods or precautions, so that the people carrying out the construction work can take them into account. | The above discussion was distilled into a roof strategy document within the health and safety file. Full specification documentation, working drawings and suppliers literature were also provided in the health and safety file |
| To identify significant hazards designers must understand how the design can be built, maintained, used and decommissioned. | Each of these aspects was debated by the team and the roof strategy statement pointed out relevant aspects which might not be immediately apparent to a competent contractor. |

**Notes to example 2:**

1   The above example shows typical output information form the examination of one particular hazard. It is indicative, not exhaustive and must only be used to facilitate understanding of the CDM work of a designer; see also Chapter 2 for guidance.

2   Note that "in-use" risks are considered here, as well as construction risks, as required by CDM2007. Guidance on workplace "in-use" considerations is available in CIRIA publication C663, *CDM2007 – Workplace "in-use" guidance for designers.*